FOREVER YOUN

How to Look and Feel
Ten Years Younger in Ten Days:
A Step by Step Programme

MARISA PEER

MICHAEL JOSEPH
LONDON

MICHAEL JOSEPH LTD

Published by the Penguin Group
27 Wrights Lane, London W8 5TZ
Viking Penguin Inc., 375 Hudson Street, New York, New York 10014, USA
Penguin Books Australia Ltd, Ringwood, Victoria, Australia
Penguin Books Canada Ltd, 10 Alcorn Avenue, Toronto, Ontario, Canada M4V 3B2
Penguin Books (NZ) Ltd, 182–190 Wairau Road, Auckland 10, New Zealand

Penguin Books Ltd, Registered Offices: Harmondsworth, Middlesex, England

First published by Michael Joseph 1997
10 9 8 7 6 5 4 1

Set in 11/13.5pt Monotype Bembo
Printed in England by Clays Ltd, St Ives plc

A CIP catalogue record for this book is available from the British Library

ISBN 0 7181 42209
The moral right of the author has been asserted

CONTENTS

ACKNOWLEDGEMENTS

This book is dedicated to my grandmother, who had the most perfect skin.

Darling Cissie, without you wherever would I be now? I owe you everything, I love you and I miss you.

Also to my daughter Phaedra, who keeps me young.

Very special thanks and acknowledgements to:

my mother who has always looked younger and is a great role model for me;

my father;

Gil Boyne, a dear friend, for showing me the power of hypnosis and being such a great mentor;

all my clients and students, from whom I have learned so much; you have taught me as much as I have ever taught you;

all the doctors and medical professionals who have always been so supportive of my work and believed in the work I do, especially to Dr Susan Horsewood Lee;

Anthony Robbins, for showing me a vision;

Dr Deepak Chopra, Dr Wayne Dyer, Dr David Viscott, Dr Ed Martin, Dr Ellen Langer, for being outstanding teachers;

Luigi and Chris, for all your support.

And most especially to you, for having the desire to change to defy ageing; this book is written for *you*.

'For each age is a dream that is dying or one that is coming to birth'

ARTHUR WILLIAM EDGAR O'SHAUGHNESSY (1844–81)

INTRODUCTION

Ageing and our awareness of it is written about in magazines and newspapers on a regular basis, reflecting what seems to have become a preoccupation with how old we feel, how old we look and how old we are. We live in a very ageist society where people are categorized by their ages.

In fact, ageing is much more of a choice than we have been led to believe since normal ageing has never been defined and what we think of as normal ageing is nothing more than abnormal conditioning. Ageing is unique and individual for each of us and not easily defined or predicted – haven't we all met or heard of people who are old or burned out, even at thirty and others who are young at eighty?

Scientists are just beginning to scratch the surface of the amazing capabilities of the mind and body. All over the world scientists are at work to discover what makes us age and how can we prevent it or slow it down, and there are regular breakthroughs in the discoveries that will help you if you wish to age more slowly. Almost daily something new comes to light in the anti-ageing field and there is so much to choose from including diet, exercise, and vitamin supplements, smart drugs, a cocktail of anti-oxidants, mountain air therapy (MAT), psycho neuro immunology, the power of thought, and a variety of other things that can delay, reverse and defy ageing as we know it.

If your desire is to look and feel younger for as long as possible, to grow older without growing old then there is an abundance of information and all kinds of new discoveries coming to light that will assist you. However, the most important tool for use in anti-ageing is the mind; the human mind is the most powerful healing force there is, no drug in the world can match it and if it were ever possible to build a computer equivalent to the human brain, it would take at least two buildings the size of the World Trade Centre just to house it.

Any steps you take in the anti-ageing field must be accompanied by a belief that you can slow down ageing and become younger. Using vitamins, diet and exercise can only work and indeed will work much better if you also use the power of your mind and your belief system to become younger.

This book will show you exactly how to do this. It is different, it is full of clearly defined, simple, workable approaches that get noticeable results easily, quickly and inexpensively. It will take you through a step by step programme that will change forever your beliefs and expectations about ageing, and as a result you will be able to look, feel and become younger at any age and at every stage of your life. *Forever Young* will show you how to take control of your thinking, how to discover and change any limiting beliefs about yourself and ageing, and how to achieve your goals of remaining younger all your life.

One of the reasons ageing is impossible to define is because our life expectancy is constantly increasing. In Stone Age times life expectancy was about eighteen years, in Roman times it was twenty-eight years. At the beginning of this century life expectancy was forty-three years for men, forty-seven years for women, and only 10 per cent of the population lived to sixty-five years (figures are from The Office of Censuses). Today life expectancy is moving towards eighty-five years for women, especially French and Japanese women, and a few years less for men. The record of living to 120 years has just been broken by a Frenchwoman, who is now 121. In slightly over fifty years we have doubled our life expectancy and it is rising rapidly. Every three months we add another month to our life expectancy or every three years we add another year to our lifespan. Not only are people living longer but they tend to have younger organs, so someone of forty today cannot be compared with someone of forty a hundred years ago, because their bodies and organs would be entirely different. They would also look very different: the forty-year-old of a hundred years ago would usually look old and tired, somewhat worn out.

With previous generations staying young was not a priority. On the whole, people had harder lives and by the time they reached their fifties they may have wanted to retire and become sedentary, since life was about surviving, raising children, having enough to eat and somewhere to live. For many people just being able to achieve this was enough and they then felt it was time to wind down.

In a relatively short period of time things have changed greatly. Better housing and sanitation, better medicine, a greater variety of food, easier working conditions and better means of transport mean that people can now reach retirement age but don't feel like retiring. They are not worn out, they still have a desire for life and don't like being old because of all the negative connotations being old is supposed to have: they may not feel particularly old or wish to be viewed as old.

Retirement no longer means the time when your life ends and you wind down and prepare for your final years; instead, it can mean another exciting chapter of life with so much we can be, do and enjoy. If we retire at sixty and live for another thirty years then we are only two-thirds of the way through our lives and knowing this can give us the incentive we need to enjoy this stage and to see all the advantages it has to offer us.

So many people dread getting old and dread retiring, because they have such negative images of what retiring means. They understandably don't like the pictures conjured up by the words *old* or *retired* and they are not words that I recommend you use –

so find something better, something descriptive in a good way. I heard a good example of this when someone called ageing 'sageing'. Since our lives are different now we can and must age differently. Retiring from work is not retiring from life and we can be older in years whilst remaining younger in attitude, with younger bodies and a younger mindset.

By the end of this century the biggest population increase in Britain will be amongst the age group of 45- to 59-year-olds, as the baby boom generation reaches that age. There will be more people of fifty than of any other age and fewer people under fifty to fill vacancies in the job market. By the year 2000 every third person in the job market will be over forty. Companies will have to rethink their ageist policies and the common complaint that those of us over forty cannot find employment will have to change and will change.

It is sad that so many people believe and find that they cannot get a job after forty because industry seems to have written them off as too old, forgetting that age forty now is equivalent to age twenty-five or thirty fifty years ago. In technology, sales, financial services and marketing, age discrimination usually begins in the thirties. Employers of older people find that they can easily do the work and don't lack enthusiasm, skill or experience but they have the mindset that their age is against them, which can become a self-fulfilling prophecy, whereas younger employees tend to have a more hopeful, positive and optimistic attitude. We must all take responsibility for changing this.

I was amazed at how prevalent ageism is in sport. At the last Olympics, every paper picked up on Linford Christie's age and frequently referred to him as a grandfather to emphasize the point that he is old. In fact he was thirty-six, which is young, but in sport it is seen as old.

Linford Christie defied the belief in sport that speed and youth go together, because he actually got faster as he got older. In his early thirties he was running faster than he had in his twenties. Sadly we have all been so conditioned into ageing beliefs that people seemed unable to understand how this could be possible.

Stu Mittleman, the world-record runner, has done a lot to change ageism in sport since he is faster in his forties than he was in his twenties and has more endurance. Every year he runs 1,000 miles in eleven days running for eighty-four miles a day over twenty-one hours and sleeping for only three hours, completing this feat with no injuries, not even blisters. He has changed the belief that we decline as we age, as he is maintaining and even improving his endurance as he gets older. Many athletes I have worked with and spoken to say that as they get older they notice that their recovery time may be a little longer, but otherwise they feel the same. In the case of Stu Mittleman his recovery time is as good as ever. He said, 'We are not limited by our age; we are liberated by it.'

Ageism is also very prevalent in tennis. Many players who probably could have continued to play well retired perhaps before they needed to, because they were conditioned to believe they were too old to beat the new younger players. This happened with Jimmy Connors and with Björn Borg. Martina Navratilova was viewed as an exception when she played into her mid thirties and her age was focused on repeatedly. As long as we view people like this as an exception, we are still in the mindset that ageing is beyond our control. Instead, we need to see people like Martina as wonderful examples of our ability to defy ageing.

Ageism exists in almost every area of sport, in the media, in the arts and in the workplace, but since we are all ageing differently and have vast potential to remain young as we become older in years, I believe that eventually ageism will become as unacceptable as sexism and racism are today. We are perhaps the first generation that is holding on to youth as we age and this is very exciting and something that we can continue to improve on and benefit from as long as we are given the specific information and instructions that will enable this to happen. This book will enable you to achieve this, to become and remain younger throughout your life.

If, like many people, you are concerned with ageing then it is worth knowing the facts. Do you know that your body does not actually age, that 98 per cent of the atoms in your body were not even there a year ago?

Our body makes:

a new skin every month,

a new skeleton every three months,

a new liver every six weeks,

a new stomach lining every four to five days;

our brain cells change yearly;

our blood renews itself every month;

our eye cells regenerate every forty-eight hours;

the raw material of our DNA changes every six weeks;

our body cells are always new.

Our body is renewing itself all the time, every second, and as we age, we are all unique, ageing on our own timetable which we have great ability to influence.

As toddlers and young children we all tend to age the same way: a hundred six-year-olds would all have the same internal organs, the same heart, lungs, muscles and kidneys. A hundred sixty-year-olds would have vastly different hearts, lungs, muscles, kidneys and other organs: some would be younger than sixty, some older, depending on their lifestyle and their ageing beliefs or expectations.

When an anonymous body is found and information is relayed to the public, a ten-year age-span will always be given. For example the news item will describe a woman between the age of thirty-five and forty-five or a man between the age of fifty and sixty, because ageing is so increasingly hard to define. How good are you at getting someone's age exactly right? Just take a look at all the people around you. Can you really get their age right, or do you, like all of us, know people who look younger than their years and others who look older?

The age you are in years is irrelevant, since we have three ages, three different ways of measuring our age. We have a chronological age, a biological age and a psychological age.

Our chronological age is the age on our birth certificate.

Our biological age is the age of our bodies and the age of our bodies' organs. Our internal organs and cells all age on their own timetable and can fluctuate greatly. For instance, people who meditate or are very calm have been proven to be twelve years younger biologically than they are chronologically, which means their organs are younger in years than the age on their birth certificate. A runner may have a younger heart and lungs than his actual age, but our organs can also be older than their owners, especially with people who live very stressful lives, drink heavily or use drugs and overuse prescription drugs. A recent study in America on a particular group of 35-year-olds showed they all had livers of fifty-year-olds due to their self-abusive lifestyles. People who take care of themselves almost always have younger organs. For example, women who have babies much later in life may have very young reproductive organs biologically rather than chronologically, while some very young women go through menopause too early so their organs are biologically older but chronologically they are young.

Our psychological age is the age we feel, and this can change from moment to moment. Listening to music from the past, dancing, laughing, being childlike (as opposed to childish) and splashing in a paddling pool or giggling all cause us to feel instantly younger. This feeling sends a message to our bodies and they literally begin to grow younger. They make younger hormones, younger chemicals – this has been documented and proven many times. Feeling stressful, on the other hand, causes us to feel and look older, and this feeling sends a very different message to our bodies. The result is an acceleration of the ageing process.

We make different chemicals when we are happy to the ones we make when we are unhappy, and these can age us or re-juvenate us, depending on our thinking. Our skin is a gland that responds to our thinking. When we fall in love, we feel young, carefree and happy and falling in love feels the same at any age whether we are seventeen or seventy. The wonderful feeling of being in love sends positive messages to our organs and we feel and act younger. We seem to glow, our skin blooms and our immune system is boosted; we find ourselves singing out loud, dancing around the kitchen, smiling at strangers and generally feeling benevolent. It has been proven that people who have certain ailments, like skin conditions, migraines and joint pain, can become free of the symptoms when they initially are in the state of falling in love.

Being depressed or grieving sends different messages to our organs and we feel and act older: our skin looks drawn, pinched, grey and our immune system suffers – our immune system is also depressed. It is no coincidence that happy, optimistic people on the whole get sick less frequently, whereas depressed, pessimistic people get sick more frequently.

Even remembering being in love or remembering trauma can release the same positive or destructive hormones and chemicals that were released during the event because of our bodies' ability to respond more to our thoughts than to actual events. In fact, events as such don't affect us, but the way we interpret an event and the meaning we choose to give to it affects us totally. We can and must change the meaning and interpretation we have given to ageing.

Our psychological age is personal; we can change in a matter of moments how we feel, which affects our physiology (our body language and posture), which in turn affects our organs.

A good example of this is when we are feeling angry or upset and then something makes us laugh. Laughter is fantastic for reversing ageing. Not only can we change how we feel in an instant, we can also choose how we feel about anything at all. This is very important and I shall be discussing it in more detail later on in the book.

Don't take on the physiology of the old, the ill, the tired or depressed, because stooping, slumping, shuffling and hunching send the wrong kind of messages to our brain, whereas being active, vital, alive, joyful sends the right kind of messages to the brain and makes the right kind of healing chemicals we need to stay young.

Only our chronological age is fixed and this should be ignored, since it is not important or even relevant. Our biological age is very much linked to our psychological age, so when we feel or act young or younger, our organs start to function and behave as young organs do, they literally begin to grow younger. However, when we feel and act old, we begin to accelerate the ageing process, so our organs grow older.

This proves that how we age has much more to do with how we are as individuals than how we are genetically, and how we are as individuals is something we can influence and change. We may not be able to change our genes but we have vast powers to change ourselves; we have the power to totally succeed or fail at ageing successfully depending on how we choose to think, act, feel and react. I find it sad when people say, 'That's how I am, I can't change. I've always been this way. It's just the way I am.' I am not referring to personality traits but to the inaccuracy that says, 'I am unable to change'. Nothing could be further from the truth. We can all change and we do change and changing our thoughts and beliefs is a gift that only humans have. Animals don't have the same awareness; they cannot influence or change their thought process, but we can, and it is such a terrible waste when people don't recognize this or act upon it.

It has been said that the major advantage and disadvantage in humans is that they have this power of choice. It is an advantage if you choose to become and stay younger and a disadvantage if you choose to believe you cannot become younger and that ageing is beyond your control.

I have changed so much since studying human behaviour and human development that sometimes I can hardly recognize the person I was, or believe that I ever used to think differently. But of course I did. I had plenty of negative thoughts and beliefs which I am happily free of now. I also used to dread getting older and now I look forward to every age.

It is so important to pay attention to our thoughts about ageing and the language we use. Our cells listen and respond to our thinking, so if you say, 'I'm too old to do that,' your mind and body will accept this literally, and thus believing you are too old, will cause you to feel and act older than you need to. However, making a very simple change to your language and saying, 'I'm too tired to do that at the moment,' will have a very different effect on your body.

Now that you are aware of these three ages, if people say to you, 'You are getting too old to do that,' or, 'Well it's only to be expected at your age,' you can quite honestly reply, 'Which particular age are you referring to? Do you mean I'm too old chronologically, biologically or psychologically?'

Our chronological age is our age in years, so let us use the example of someone who is fifty. Let us imagine this fifty-year-old woman, whom we will call Sara, exercises, eats healthy food and is predominantly happy and calm. She does Yoga and has a relaxation programme that could involve massage, meditation or self-hypnosis and she is a firm believer in the power of positive thinking and has good relationships.

Although Sara is chronologically fifty, biologically she could be as young as thirty-five – her organs are younger than her birth certificate. If we were to look at her lungs, heart, skin, hair, teeth, liver, kidneys, eyes and a variety of other organs, they would not all be fifty; in fact, they would vary greatly between fifty and thirty-five. Her hair, nails and teeth are younger than fifty, her heart and lungs are younger than fifty because she exercises, and let us assume she has protected her skin from the sun, so her skin is younger than fifty. She drinks a lot of water, so her kidneys are less than fifty, and she is moderate with alcohol, so her liver is younger too. This woman is not fanatical, but she is taking control of how she ages in a very beneficial way and she has a good immune system, good circulation and good digestion and takes the time to breathe properly.

Now let us imagine a colleague of hers, also fifty years old according to her birth certificate. Let us call her Jill. She doesn't exercise, her diet is unhealthy and she lives a very stressful life most of the time. Her job and family life are stressful – perhaps she relaxes by smoking, having a drink or taking a sunbed session.

Although Jill like Sara is chronologically fifty, biologically she could be much older. Her organs could be far older than her chronological age. If we were to look at her lungs, heart, skin, hair, teeth, liver, kidneys, eyes and a variety of other organs, they would not all be fifty. In fact, they would vary greatly between less than fifty and frequently more than fifty. Her nails and teeth could still be younger than fifty, while her heart and lungs are more than fifty, because she smokes and does not exercise. And if we assume she has not protected her skin from the sun and has sunbathed frequently then her skin will be quite a lot older than fifty. She drinks a lot of alcohol and not enough water, so her kidneys are above fifty as is her liver. Her immune system is not good, because of her stress levels and because she breathes in a shallow way, and this, along with a poor diet, causes her to have poor digestion, which can disrupt all the systems of her body, ageing her prematurely. This woman is not an extreme case; many people live this way but she is failing to take control of how she ages and is ageing ahead of her chronological age.

These examples show you that your chronological age is not linked to your biological age and you are not your age in years and can cease to pay attention to that number. The age you are biologically is of far more importance than the age you are in years, your chronological age. Now let us imagine that Sara feels young and believes that she is young, she laughs a lot, sings out loud, does young things, fun things, by playing tennis, going dancing, listening to music that makes her feel alive, vital and joyful. She controls her state and has a positive attitude and seems to find the good in a situation. If she is stuck in traffic she listens to some music, makes some notes or strikes up conversation or decides not to feel upset since the traffic is beyond her control, but her ability to choose what she thinks is hers to control and she does this successfully. She tells herself she is young, that she looks and feels young. She feels young psychologically and does not allow thoughts of her age to stop her doing things. Because she feels young psychologically this has a very positive effect on her organs, which respond to the way she thinks and feels by becoming younger.

Jill is very aware of getting older and allows thoughts of her age to influence what she does. She tells herself she is too old to do some things she might enjoy doing, she mentions her age far too much and thinks about it too much. It is the first thing she considers when new opportunities or invitations are presented to her. If her legs ache she tells herself she's getting old, without realizing that this one thought is accelerating the ageing process. If she's invited to go on a trip she thinks she may be too old for the walking it could involve, or too old to mix with the others who perhaps are all younger. She tells herself she is too old and will look foolish if she takes up roller-skating.

She turns down loud music, telling herself she has grown out of that or is past the age for such things. If she is stuck in traffic she feels helpless and frustrated if she forgets things and she tells herself it's all because of her age. Jill has not learned to control her state, her attitude can be negative. This has a detrimental effect on her organs, which respond to the way she thinks and feels by becoming older.

The number of years you have lived on this earth is not the age of your body, your mind or your emotions. We all feel so many different ages at different times, why would we categorize ourselves by the least important one, the one based on our birth certificate? When I am going on stage to give a seminar I feel so excited: it's like going on a first date and I feel about seventeen. When I am playing with my daughter I feel about ten. When I have to deal with a lot of responsibility, or don't like my nanny's new music, or I have not had enough sleep, I can feel much older.

As you read the examples of Sara and Jill, you may be thinking: I sunbathe and drink, my diet isn't great, what is the point of this book? Reading this is making me think I'm already biologically older than I should be. The point is that the power of your mind and your ability to think different thoughts can override this. You may have heard of people who do unhealthy things yet remain young because they have a zest for life and an amazing attitude and you can do the same because positive thinking has been proved to counteract even some negative habits.

If you are serious about becoming and remaining younger, it is a good idea to make some lifestyle changes as well. The last chapter of this book will show you some lifestyle changes that are easy to make, that are not fanatical and that will have an additional impact on the changes you are making.

As you read this book you will notice it is divided into three specific parts.

Part One is titled Preparation.

Part Two is titled Understanding.

Part Three is titled Action.

In Part One you will be given a lot of factual information that will allow you to see how and why ageing as we think we know it is a misconception and a fallacy. You will engage in some easy, fun tests that enable you to change your thoughts and beliefs. This first section is preparing you and getting you ready to change and to become younger. This section covers much of the ground-work necessary for you to change not just mentally but physically too; you will actually be able to change your biochemistry once you have gone through these three days of preparation.

In Part Two you will gain a great insight into how the mind works, which will allow you to understand how your mind works, and how this is directly related to how you are ageing. You will be shown in a very easy step by step approach how to direct your mind and how to remain physically young and how to stay young mentally. You will learn how to make affirmations work for you, how to visualize perfectly, how to programme your own subconscious mind and how to develop a programme unique to you that will allow you to become and stay younger.

In Part Three you will be taking action to become younger. You will be able to put yourself into a heightened state of aware-ness where you can influence your subconscious mind in the most positive way. You will learn how to communicate with your cells so that they respond by becoming younger. You will be shown how to test your biological age and be given a test that will show you how you are ageing to date. You will learn the impor-tance of goals in slowing down ageing and you will learn how important lifestyle is in reversing your age. You will be shown lifestyle changes that you can quite easily make and these will include Diet, Exercise, Vitamins, Digestion, Electricity and Sleep.

You may buy this book with every intention of completing it within ten days, but if your workload is demanding you may prefer to do it over ten weeks, and you could do it over a longer period if you prefer. However you decide to complete this programme it is most important that you do each exercise one step at a time and complete each and every exercise for that day before you move on to the next step or day. The challenge with not doing this programme over ten consecutive days or weeks is that you will no longer have regular spaced intervals in which to complete the exercises and you may begin to work through the book erratically. Do endeavour to complete this programme over ten days or ten weeks and if you do it over ten weeks set aside the same day, e.g. Sunday morning or Wednesday evening, so it becomes almost like a ritual for you. You will lose your momentum if you do the first three steps then leave the book only to return some weeks later to complete the other steps and you will also lose the impact the programme would have had on your body. You will only need to spend about an hour a day, so please make the time. You will be so glad you did not just ten days or ten weeks from now, but ten and twenty years from now, when you will still be reaping the benefits.

This book has been written and designed in ways that make it straightforward, with easy-to-read and easy-to-follow techniques. As you follow the day by day, step by step approach you will easily know what you are to do and where you are in the programme at every step and at each day.

The chapters of the book are designed to lead you easily from one step into the next. The sequence of this book has been specifically worked out and it is very important indeed that you follow the sequence as it is written. Only go on to the next step or day after you have completed the previous one, only begin each exercise after you have completed the exercise that preceded it.

I know it is tempting to read the book from cover to cover

with the intention of then returning to it and then doing the exercise but you will get better results if you follow the programme as written. It may also be tempting to do all the exercises in one go, even in one day. Please don't do this. Remember these exercises need to be done systematically and in sequence and that each day you are taking on board new information and giving your mind time to process it and absorb it before you absorb further new information the following day or week.

Taking the day by day, step by step approach will give you the time to change and will excite your imagination and excite your subconscious mind and make you ready for, and receptive to, changing both physically and mentally. The ability to excite the subconscious mind is a great asset in implementing positive permanent changes.

It has been proved that people learn much better and absorb much more information in concentrated periods of forty-five minutes, than they do over several uninterrupted hours. You will learn and take in much more if you spend an hour or so with the book working on each chapter daily than if you were to spend ten hours with it all at once. A lot of research has gone into the structure of this book for your benefit, so please adhere to this structure.

Since most change is retroactive and cumulative, you may not notice immediate changes taking place. But they will be taking place, so don't give up the programme. If you stay with it you will get results. We don't notice headaches going but we notice they have gone; we can lie in bed listening to a car alarm ringing then notice it has stopped, but yet not notice the moment when it stopped. These are examples of change being retroactive. People only notice they feel better when they are better but often not during the process itself; this applies with illness, grief, pain, loss, anxiety etc. We notice change mostly afterwards, as we look back on how we have changed, rather than as we are changing and it can be hard to pinpoint the moment or time when the process of changing occurred or even began.

An important point to remember as you go through this

programme is that you will be slowing down and reversing ageing inside your body, which will then effect visible outer changes.
In the West we are very caught up with how we look on the outside, and while it is important to care about how we look, it is
more important to work from inside our bodies than to only concentrate on the outside, on our skin, hair and appearance.

As you participate in this programme you will expect to feel
younger, to become younger and of course to look younger and
you will. But you need to be aware that the most important
changes, the age reversal of your organs, will be going on within
your body and you may not see results immediately – but they
will be there. Some of the most important changes may not show
their impact for years, changes that can help you maintain hearing, eyesight and agility throughout your life.

Throughout this book I will tell you to follow the instructions
exactly as they are laid out, to read the chapters on each succes-
sive day and to complete the mental and physical exercises each
day as you arrive at them. By following these clear and easy to
adhere to instructions you can become ten years younger in ten
days, as you change your beliefs, your thinking, and alter in a
positive way the images and thoughts you have about ageing.
Your mind will form a different concept of ageing, and since your
mind controls your body, you will be able to physically and
mentally change.

There are some things you require along with this book and
they are a pen, a notebook or exercise book, a desire to become
younger and a commitment to follow through; this is the most
important tool of all. You must commit yourself to doing the programme each day and to doing the exercises each day as they are
laid out for you.

If you have:

the *Conviction* that you can slow ageing;

the *Desire* to adhere to this programme;

the *Belief*, the *Faith* that it works, that you have the ability
within you to change your body and this book will give you
that belief;

the ability to *begin* it, to *complete* it, to *follow through* every day, to *persist* in changing your thinking;
then you absolutely cannot fail in becoming younger.

You may not have these things as you begin reading this book but you will certainly have them when you have finished the book.

Keep a journal or exercise book and your pen always to hand with the book. Don't use loose sheets of paper, as you may lose them; having a journal or workbook will allow you to continue to review your thoughts, beliefs and expectations and to look back and review your writings at any time so your workbook will become a manual that you can return to and use as an invaluable reference.

Writing is very important. Most successful people think on paper, others keep things in their minds. When you hold something in your mind it is a wish, a daydream, a fantasy, but when you write it out and commit it to paper it becomes more real as you can look at it, revise it. Also, writing things down causes the conscious mind to accept them and the subconscious mind to go to work and make them become a reality.

This book does not promise quick results that are not sustained. Providing you make the changes required and allow these changes to become a part of your life you will be able to stay younger. If you began an exercise programme that promised you a flatter stomach or firmer thighs you would not quit the programme once you had achieved your goal. I imagine you would stay on a maintaining programme that allowed you to keep the results you had worked for and the same is true with my programme.

You can and will keep the results you achieve through using this book as long as you keep using the concept of this book and keep hearing the messages it contains about ageing. Because of the wealth of information contained within this book, and the definite results you will see and feel as a result of following the programme, you will benefit by returning to this book over and over again. It is worth re-reading sections of this book or the complete book from time to time to remind yourself of the power of thought and the effect it has on you. As well as reading chapters over and over again it is also excellent to read the things you have written again and again and to review and recap on them whenever you wish to.

When you are making physical changes such as exercising for suppleness or weight-training for strength it is absolutely true that the more effort you put in, the better and quicker the results you get. When you are making mental changes and changing your thinking, the opposite applies. You don't have to work or to push yourself, you don't need to make a huge effort at all. Making mental changes is quite the opposite of the 'no pain no gain' theory. As long as you are open to the possibility of changing your thinking, you will be able to change your thinking. Thoughts can be changed in seconds, even thoughts we may have held for years, and this book will show you how to do that.

This programme is simple, easy, painless and enjoyable, since it requires you to focus and to absorb some new ideas, to be open to change, to be receptive to new possibilities, and if humans were not already programmed to do this almost as second nature we would not have cars, aeroplanes, electricity or sanitation and would still eat with our fingers and live in huts.

There is nothing complicated or difficult about this programme. In fact, many of my patients/clients find it so easy that the most frequent response I hear is, 'I wish I had known about this earlier. I am amazed at how easy it is and how much better I feel having used it; it is so simple yet so very effective.'

I hesitate to use the word *persevere* as I tell you that it is absolutely worth persevering with this programme because it can and does work, since the word *persevere* may give you the idea that this book entails hard work. In fact, most of the things I will be asking you to do in this book are easy, fairly quick, sometimes instantaneous and frequently fun, and involve little or no financial outlay.

Implementing these changes and making them a part of your life will have a remarkable effect on how you look and age. The best news is that some of the changes that are the most simple to make will be the ones that have the most impact on slowing down the rate at which you age. By using the techniques in this book you can consistently look and feel much younger whilst adding thirty or more years to your life. You can look and feel vibrant, healthy and active into your eighties and beyond. You can live to enjoy more and more birthdays, yet be younger than many of your contemporaries and you can help to change the view of ageing which is based on misconception. This is especially important to women, who are judged much more than men on their looks and on their youth. This is slowly changing and you can do much to change it further, since to change any view collectively, we first have to change it individually.

There are some wonderful women who have already changed our view of women as they age, women like Goldie Hawn, Felicity Kendall, Francesca Annis and Joanna Lumley, who have made fifty sexy and youthful, and Tina Turner, who turns on its head the belief that we run out of energy as we age. Isn't it exciting to know that you can have the same impact on others as you change your own beliefs? We can help ensure that ageless women (and men) become the rule rather than the exception.

You are about to begin your first day, so feel excited, enthusiastic and positive; you are about to do something wonderful and powerful for you. You are going to change for ever the way you see yourself and you are going to change the way others see you. You are also going to change the way you feel because you are ready now to move into reading *Forever Young*. As long as you use this book correctly, you will become Forever Young.

PART ONE

Preparation

DAY 1

Changing Your Thoughts

Think and Grow Young

On Day One we are going to cover what is probably the most important step in how to slow down the ageing process: Changing Your Thoughts. It is certainly the easiest to put into practice, since it requires no financial outlay and no long periods of your time need to be devoted to it. Furthermore, when you begin to see how easy it is to change your thinking, you will find it creeping into other areas of your life with wonderful results.

Thoughts are things and all our thoughts have consequences; in fact, a thought is a cause set in motion within us. Our thoughts, beliefs and expectations about ageing will have a huge effect on how we age, since our body is set up to mirror what is going on in our mind.

The strongest, most powerful force in the mind is its need to act in ways which match our thinking, and the strongest force in the human personality is the need to remain consistent with how we define ourselves. In other words, your body responds to the pictures you are making in your mind and constantly works to meet the picture, while the subconscious mind has little capacity to reason and believes whatever we tell it. What we think we are we can become.

The subconscious mind has no sense of humour either, so if

you think *I look ancient in this*, even if you joke just to yourself about getting older, your mind will always take you literally since that is what it is set up to do. Now your mind has to make a picture of the word *ancient*, which it will probably see as something very old and fragile and not at all the image you want for yourself. Since I know that you can't possibly want to see yourself as ancient, you must stop thinking those thoughts and using those words.

Many of you will say *How do I stop thinking a thought, since it is instant?* It will get easier, I promise, and you can help by dismissing every negative thought about ageing you have and replacing it with a new, constructive one instead. Your thoughts belong to you – why keep them if you don't want them and don't want to believe them? Your thoughts are yours to change.

What we see we become, and what we think about all the time we become, so think about being younger and you will be younger. It sounds almost too simple, doesn't it? But it works – the power of thought may be simple, but thoughts themselves are enormously powerful and enormously effective. You cannot have thoughts and feelings without them being expressed in the body.

We can all take charge of programming our minds because the way we feel from one moment to the next is a result of two things: the pictures we make in our head and the words we are using. The mind especially responds to thoughts, words and images that are symbolic.

The good news is that you are able to choose the pictures you make in your mind, to choose what you say, think and feel about ageing. Only humans have this ability, and through your power of choice, through your ability to choose your thoughts and beliefs about ageing, you can succeed in becoming and remaining younger at every stage of your life.

Even with habits, the habit of thought precedes the habit of action, meaning that if you believe you have to smoke to concentrate, or drink to relax, that belief will eventually become more powerful than the habit itself. This is why when changing habits you must also change the beliefs related to the habits, thus ensuring that you don't return to them.

If you are going to exercise classes to retain a youthful figure and muscle tone, or taking antioxidants to fight ageing but doubt their ability to work, or believe that ageing is inevitable, then these thoughts can and will work against all the work you are doing. However, if you believe that you will influence how you age, if you decide to change your thinking, if you change your habits of thought and also change habits of action like lifestyle, nutrition and vitamins, you can expect to achieve wonderful results that stay with you throughout your life.

Because of the mind's ability to believe and accept without question, to accept as an absolute fact all our thoughts and dialogue including the internal dialogue or self-talk that goes on inside our heads, it follows that if you constantly tell yourself you are getting old you will become that way, whereas if you keep telling yourself you are remaining youthful you will stay that way instead.

If you tell yourself you are forgetful or clumsy you will become that way at any age, and even telling this to young children can cause them to act and become clumsy and forgetful. If you tell yourself you are forgetful because you are getting older, you will begin to identify and act in ways that match that thinking. If you decide you may be showing early signs of Alzheimer's or Parkinson's disease, you must abandon that thought immediately – don't even entertain the idea or put words or pictures relating to it in your mind.

Some doctors believe that when migraines, depression, or period pains run in families it is because the mind has accepted this as inevitable and the body acts accordingly. So often when working with clients they tell me things like: *Everyone in my family has allergies*, or *All the women in my family have had problems conceiving*, or *My mother suffered terribly with sinus pain and I'm just like her*, and so on, without being aware of how they are identifying with the symptom.

Of course there are illnesses that are passed through families but it is very important not to identify with something you don't want, especially in the area of our health and ageing.

With children, saying *He has a temper just like his father*, or *She has problems spelling just like me*, or *He has a nervous stomach like his grandfather* puts that into their identity, which is exactly what you don't want. As you will see later in this book, identity beliefs affect everything we do and are extremely powerful.

The body must match what is going on in the mind, never the other way around; the mind won't match what is going on in the body, since thought always has to come first and every thought eventually becomes expressed in the body or through the body.

Ageing has become an expectation that we live up to in our minds and then in our bodies. The way you expect to age and the beliefs you hold about ageing are having an enormous effect on how you age right now. It has been said that the body you have today is a result of the thoughts you were thinking about ageing ten years ago, and the body you will have in ten years time will be a result of the thoughts you are thinking about ageing now.

Thoughts and beliefs on ageing affect us greatly; your thoughts about ageing are affecting your body this very second. The body mimics the mind's thoughts. Every thought we have creates a physical reaction in the body and an emotional response, but our thoughts and beliefs are not fixed and are ours to change. Thinking young thoughts, telling yourself your cells are young, causes them to respond, to act and behave as young cells do. Our cells listen and respond to our thinking, so if you come in from a long or tiring day having planned to go out that evening and think to yourself or say to anyone listening *I'm too old to go out in the evenings any more*, your mind and body will accept this literally and thus, believing you are too old, will cause you to feel and act older than you need to.

However, making a very simple change to your thoughts and thinking *I'm too tired to go out this evening* will have a very different effect on your body, since it is a temporary rather than permanent feeling and belief. It does not mean that you will be too tired tomorrow.

It isn't always automatic to change our thinking. Sometimes we have to keep at it because we have been conditioned to believe ageing is unavoidable.

Even I, who of all people should know better, still catch myself blaming age occasionally. As I came out of the gym recently my knee twinged and my instant thought was *My knees are getting older.* Our thoughts are so instant it is easy to feel that they are running us. But we must think: *Where did that belief come from? Who put it there? Why am I choosing to believe this?* As I had the thought I had to immediately dismiss it, then replace it, by reminding myself that joints can ache or twinge at any age.

We can use power of the mind to stay youthful, active and healthy, so we are young whatever our years. You can choose to believe that youth is energy, flexibility and attitude, to know that if you think old thoughts and use ageing language you will become old, and therefore make doing the opposite a lifelong habit. You will have to work at this initially but it will become second nature after a while and will be worth it.

Since our body doesn't age in the way we have been led to believe, and since the mind can be ageless, it renders pointless all the beliefs and negative expectations we have learnt and falsely hold to be true about ageing.

Because we all age uniquely, we must change for ever these self-limiting beliefs about ageing which exist only in our imagination. After all, our thoughts and beliefs are absolutely ours to change – just because we have held something to be true for a number of years is not a good enough reason to hold on to it any longer. You used to believe in Santa Claus once, and then changed your beliefs as you acquired new information. We can always control our thoughts and what things mean and then anything is possible.

The human nervous system is the only nervous system aware of ageing. However, we can use that same awareness to influence our cells and to slow down ageing. We must never despair of or dread growing old, as it will make us age more quickly. We are only ever as old as we think we are, since our cells process our thoughts and we eventually turn into our beliefs.

It is the same if we believe that we are fat or unlovable – we move towards the thoughts we are holding until we eventually become a living, walking, talking expression of them. A belief or feeling that we are unlovable is the common denominator of most emotional problems in the world, so if you think only youth is desirable, an image that advertisers sell to us relentlessly, if you think that only youth is lovable then it is not surprising that you may dread ageing. However, ageing today is new and different. It has been called the New Old Age, simply because old age now is a different experience, and for many people it is a positive, healthy and enjoyable time of life. I think it would be more enjoyable still if the words *old age* were used less and something with a more positive image was used instead. The *New Old Age* is better. *Sageing* is better.

Ageing no longer needs to be feared as deteriorating or becoming sedentary and fragile. It can be quite different, and for many of us it already is.

Everything we do and want is to do with how it makes us feel. We want money, status and youth because we believe they will make us feel better. Changing your thoughts about how you are going to age will undoubtedly cause you to feel better physically, mentally and emotionally.

The power of thought alone can change the physical body and affect our mental health and our immune system. What we think is possible affects our body, and we sometimes come across events where people get drunk on alcohol-free beverages because they think they are potent, or high on nothing but their thoughts or beliefs about the substance they are ingesting. This thought process can become even stronger when it occurs in groups – mass sickness can occur on airlines or at functions and at receptions, and the same thing can happen with mass hysteria or anger.

During a game at the Monterey Park football stadium in Los Angeles, several people became ill with symptoms of food poisoning. The on-site doctor treating them found that they had all drunk Coca-Cola from the vending machines at the stadium and decided that fermentation or contamination might have taken place within the dispensing machine. Eager that no one else be put at risk, he had an announcement put out requesting that no one drink from the machines because of the illness and had the symptoms described over the air. Almost at once the stadium became a sea of retching and fainting, the sufferers including people who had not drunk anything from the suspected machines. Five ambulances carried people back and forth between the hospital and the stadium, until it was discovered that the vending machines were safe and the illness of the first group was unrelated.

Thoughts are very powerful and have very direct consequences. Drug companies have to discard over 33 per cent of drug test results, because if a person believes a drug to be effective that can have more effect on him than the drug itself. This has a connection with why many repeat drug prescriptions are placebos and why whenever a drug is tested it must also be tested on a control group, who think they are receiving the same drug but are receiving a placebo instead.

Our belief about the drugs and medicines we take can be even more significant in our recovery than the pharmaceutical components of the drugs themselves. Dr Henry Beecher, from Harvard University, became famous for doing extensive research and numerous studies that concluded that while we may believe a particular drug has healed or cured us, in fact our belief system was the real healing force that made us well. He went on record to say: *A drug's usefulness is a direct result of not only the chemical properties of the drug, but also the patient's belief in the usefulness and effectiveness of the drug.*

In America, when a new drug which was formulated to regrow hair was tested, the group given placebo pills regrew hair despite many of them having been bald for years. In another test, in England, a group believing they were receiving a new form of chemotherapy lost all their hair purely because they expected to, since unknown to them they were also receiving placebos.

Our brain converts our expectations into chemical realities. Thoughts are things and thoughts always have an effect on our bodies: thinking about hunger, sex, tiredness, etc. will often cause us to generate feelings and physical reactions linked to our thinking. Reading books that describe immense cold can make us shiver and get goose bumps, while watching a scary or emotional film can generate feelings of fear or emotion within ourselves that seem quite real.

Of course advertising companies know all about this and use it to their advantage rather than ours. Images of food can cause us to feel hungry, images of drinks make us thirsty.

Even very young children have been shown to respond to adverts; in fact one of the reasons the children's television programme *Sesame Street* was devised was because of young children's ability to respond to television adverts. The same successful format of short bursts of message, sound and colour used to make adverts were used to make this programme.

We see even more examples of the power of thought with telepathy, and with people who we believe have unusual powers, such as faith-healers and mind-readers. I believe in faith-healing and in places like Lourdes, for example, but I also believe that just being around someone we perceive as powerful or being in a place like Lourdes can have such a powerful effect on the belief system that we can get results regardless of what is real and what is imagined.

Years ago a client came to see me because he wanted to stop drinking. He sat on the other side of my desk while I asked him some questions. Suddenly he looked at me and said, *I can't answer any more questions, this hypnosis is too powerful*, and slumped back in his chair, closed his eyes and went into a trance purely because he expected to – in fact I had not hypnotized him. Since he was already responding to his own power of thought, I used the situation to convince his subconscious that he would not drink again, as well as uncovering the causes of drinking and the beliefs that made him drink too much. He called me some weeks later to tell me how thrilled he was that he did not even want to drink any more, and to this day I still have clients who come in referred by this man. They always tell me that he is a major fan of hypnosis and of me, since I had such a powerful effect on him. I didn't ever have the heart to tell him that I did very little. His own belief system stopped him drinking.

Further examples of this are apparent in other cultures, where people may think they have been cursed and then develop symptoms and even die. In Africa this is known as shaking or pointing the bone; if the witch-doctor shakes the bone the recipient of this will expect to get ill and perhaps die, and is in fact very likely to do so. Even in cases where medical intervention has taken place to cure the resulting illness or symptoms, it hasn't always been enough, because drugs and medication cannot always overcome that person's belief system, which thinks, *I am cursed and dying*.

People who have moved to somewhere like Haiti and scorned the belief in voodoo or black magic eventually change their minds, because it is all around them, and so they become somewhat influenced by it. Other common examples include the symptoms of phantom pregnancy and psychosomatic illness.

A thought is a cause set in motion within us. Shakespeare said: *As a man thinketh he becometh*. The same thing is quoted in the Bible.

Dr Ellen Langer, a psychologist at Harvard Medical School, put this to the test when she took a group of men, all over 75, to a retreat in the country for seven days. Prior to leaving, the group were put through a series of tests to establish their bio-logical age. Among other things, they were tested for hearing, vision, grip, finger length, muscle mass, bone density, percep-tion, physical strength, blood, hormones, etc.

At the retreat they all acted as if it was 1959 instead of 1979, by wearing badges of themselves as they were twenty years ago, by watching films, sitcoms and newsreels and listening to music of the fifties. All the magazines and newspapers were from the fifties and the participants were not allowed to bring any periodicals, books or photos dated after 1959 with them.

By willingly participating in and living this experiment, they were subconsciously tricking themselves and consequently their cells into believing they were younger. During and at the end of the seven days they were put through the same tests again, and had all reversed their biological age by a minimum of seven years. Some had reversed their age by over ten years.

The retreat had been deliberately designed and furnished as it would have been twenty years earlier, to assist the group as they purposefully pretended it was twenty years ago. The conversation and everything else going on around them were deliberately designed to enable and encourage each man to act as he had when he was 55 rather than 75.

A control group went to the same retreat, but they did not have to pretend or live in an environment that was set up to mirror 1959. They improved very marginally in a few areas, but declined in others.

Ellen Langer wrote a book documenting this experiment called *Mindfulness*. This book talks about the need for newness, surprise and variety in order to stay young, and demonstrates how if we stop creating we stop living and as a consequence age faster.

Since the first group proved that we can become biologically seven years younger and more in seven days, we can learn a lot from them. You can do the same thing: you can become biologically and physically younger by changing your beliefs and recreating your thoughts of who you are and what you associate with ageing. Changing your focus and your language will slow down the way you age and has been proved to reverse it. Thoughts always affect the skin, which is why it blooms when we are in love, or feeling happy and good about ourselves, and looks grey or drawn when we are grieving or deeply unhappy.

Scientific tests showed that people who were anxious began to look older within just a few months, but when they resolved the cause of the anxiety they began to reverse this premature ageing and returned to looking younger even more rapidly.

So change your thoughts about your age; delete all negative words connected to ageing from your vocabulary; if you look in the mirror and think *My skin looks old*, decide instead that your skin looks tired – it does get tired, but has wonderful re-juvenating abilities. By changing your thinking you can absolutely change your body, since beliefs create biology and the mind is the most powerful healing force there is.

You could even create a kind of Ellen Langer retreat in your home, or even in one corner of one room, by putting up photos of you at your most agile and vital, along with some pictures of you as a child, especially pictures where you looked carefree and spontaneous. You could also have some poems or words from your favourite songs, about how youth is a state of mind.

The best thing you could do would be to make a poster or collage by cutting out pictures that symbolize or represent the kind of youthfulness you plan to achieve. Include in this collage role models, people who are similar to you in age but look and act younger. Find pictures from magazines of older people skiing or roller-blading and include them. Stick on to the collage the words or poems that inspire you to be young; find some quotes that you like or copy some from this book on to your poster. You can also write or stick on to the poster the affirmations and goals and your personal programme for becoming Forever Young that you will learn later in this book.

Woman frequently reach their thirties and then begin a life-long and destructive habit of saying: *I'm too old to wear that now . . . too old to go there any longer . . . too old for that*. Around us we hear others saying *Act your age* or *You shouldn't be doing that at your age* or *Aren't you a little old to be doing that?* No one would say that to Tina Turner, who is happier and more attractive at 56 than she was in her thirties. She is regarded as an exception, but she is not – she is a great example of how changing our thinking changes our reality. How do we know that Tina Turner is not an example of how normal ageing could look? Perhaps we are the exceptions – no one can say for sure that this is impossible.

Thoughts even affect our immune system. By changing the way we think and by changing our beliefs, by changing our language and by making some changes in the way we eat, sleep and behave, we can add thirty or even fifty full and youthful years to our lives.

Of course most people don't want to live to 100 if their quality of life is awful. However, we can live longer and stay much younger, we can continue to look and feel five, ten, eventually even fifteen years younger than we are, by changing our thinking and making the changes in this book. Just knowing that life expectancy is rapidly increasing means that middle age, which used to be from the mid-thirties onwards, now does not even need to begin until we are in our fifties. Doesn't just knowing that make you feel younger already?

If you want to change anything about your body, health, weight, relationships, first you must change your thinking. Everything that is going on in your body, including ageing, has to start with the mind, and in any area of your life that you want to change or control you must begin by changing your thoughts.

thoughts control feelings • feelings control actions • actions control events

If you start to think differently about ageing you will feel differently, which will make events different. I don't really like the word control and avoid using it, but there are certain areas such as health and ageing where it is essential that we take control of our health. In life so many things appear to be out of our control; in fact, the only real control we have over events is what we choose to think of them, what we decide something means, because the way we interpret an event or the meaning we attach to an event will affect us more than the event itself.

So thinking good thoughts about ageing, interpreting ageing differently because we are ageing differently and better than ever before, believing that we can get older without getting old, that we can look, feel and become younger, will have an immediate, ultimately visible and lasting effect on the body. I've been telling you for several pages that every thought you have has a physical effect and an emotional response within the body – now I would like to show you how true this is, since seeing is believing.

Because today is your first day, Day One in your programme of looking and feeling younger, I would like you to do a few very simple and perfectly safe exercises to demonstrate to you the amazing and physical power of thought so that you can feel it and experience it for yourself rather than just reading about it.

Physical Exercise

EXERCISE 1

Stand up with your feet slightly apart. Close your eyes and begin to imagine that just behind you is a huge magnet pulling you and rocking you backwards. Really focus on the magnet – see it as a huge U shape with the red paint on the ends just behind your shoulder blades. You will almost immediately feel yourself swaying and rocking and tipping backwards. Now imagine the magnet has moved to just under your chin, pulling you forwards. Again, as you think about the magnet pulling you forwards, your own power of thought will cause you to rock forward, to sway forwards.

Now imagine the magnet has moved to your left, then to your right shoulder, and notice your body swaying in that direction. Of course, the more you focus on the magnet, the stronger the pull will become.

If you prefer, you can close your eyes and ask a friend to describe a magnet behind you, then in front of you, then at either side of your shoulder, or ask someone to read this section to you.

Of course there is no magnet there, but you are beginning to see, to feel for yourself, your mind's ability to accept whatever you tell it, whether based on fact or fiction. As your mind accepts the thought of the magnet, it goes to work to have you react to it, even though it only exists in your imagination.

And the same is true with every thought that you have. If you think of being younger, of becoming younger, your mind has to go to work to make you, and even more importantly your cells and your immune system, react to the thought. If you think of being older the same thing happens, so one thought can generate positive reactions and another thought will generate negative reactions within the body. Whether these thoughts are based on fact or fiction is irrelevant to the mind because it cannot tell the difference.

Here is another safe and simple exercise to prove to you that thought really is the most powerful thing.

EXERCISE 2

You can do this sitting or standing. Close your eyes, stretch both hands out in front of you at shoulder height, and close both hands as if you are holding something in each hand. Now begin to imagine that in your left hand you are holding an enormous red fire-bucket filled with about 40 lb of heavy wet sand. Feel the weight of that bucket in your fingers, feel the weight moving up to your wrist, your elbow, and now your shoulder, feel it getting heavier and heavier by the second, and notice that your arm is being pulled down by the weight of the bucket. The more you focus on the bucket, on its colour and size and contents, the heavier your arm is becoming and the more it is being drawn downwards. As your left arm continues moving downwards, imagine that you are holding in your right arm the hugest helium-filled balloon. See the balloon's colour, see it as almost bigger than you are, feel the string in your hand. Because helium is lighter than air and because this balloon is firmly held in your right hand you will notice that your right arm is moving upwards, lifting upwards, travelling up higher and higher, becoming lighter and lighter, almost floating upwards of its own accord. As you think about the balloon and bucket notice the difference in your arms – one is heavy, one is light, one is moving up, the other is moving down, and the cause of this is your thought process. You may prefer to memorize this or to have someone read this part to you, as you keep your eyes shut. Again the point is to show you how easy it is to influence your mind, and to prove to you that thoughts have a very real effect on our bodies.

Thoughts affect chemical changes in the body. Positive thinking can produce chemicals in the brain and the cells of the central nervous system which then affect the immune system. This can then produce NK cells, T-cells and white blood cells which can destroy certain types of illness and fight bacteria and viruses.

As the strongest force in the mind is its need to make us act in ways that match our thinking, it is vital to change any negative thoughts, beliefs and expectations connected with ageing.

So you must:

Focus on how you want to be, never on how you don't want to be.

In other words:

Keep your mind on how you want to age and off how you don't want to age.

Therefore with ageing and in all areas of life:

Focus only on what you want to move towards and accomplish.

Never on the opposite, which is what you want to leave behind.

This becomes easier as you find the flip side of every negative thought and use that instead.

- Whatever we focus on we move towards.
- Whatever we focus on we experience and feel.
- Whatever we focus on we get more of, it becomes more real to us.

If you focus on having an injection, or on the pressure in your ears during flight descent, you can make it painful, even very painful, but if you focus on something else you may not even notice the sensations.

Mental Exercise

EXERCISE 1

Using your diary or notebook, write out all your thoughts about ageing related to you.

Write out every negative thought that you have been led to believe about ageing on one page.

Write out new, more appropriate thoughts on the opposite page.

Keep writing until you have run out of thoughts, but don't be surprised if more come to you later; as they do, write them out into your notebook.

The reason I want you to write out negative thoughts is because often we are not even aware of our thoughts. We hold them, we act from them, but we don't confront them or look at them or think *Is this relevant to me? Has it ever been relevant to me?*

We revamp our wardrobes and update our homes, yet fail to update our thinking. Before we can change our thinking we need to identify and discover our thoughts. This chapter will allow you to become more and more aware of your thoughts in order to update them, to review and revise them.

Take some time to uncover your thoughts about how you are ageing – become more and more aware of how you think.

Find and root out any negative thoughts, confront them, change them, eliminate and eradicate them. As you start writing your thoughts will begin to flow from you; at this stage don't stop to analyse them, just keep on writing, stopping to pull up more thoughts and writing them out. It does not matter if you write out reams of thoughts or just a few, as long as they are *your* thoughts. The most important thing is to write out what you think about ageing, what your point of view about ageing is.

This book will allow you to use the new knowledge and facts within it to destroy your old negative thinking. In its place you will have new, powerful, positive thoughts that you really believe in and that affect your biology in the most wonderful way. You will use your wonderful mind to tell yourself you are becoming younger, instead of rationalizing why you have to get older.

Below are some examples to give you an idea and to get you started on the process of changing your thinking.

Examples of Negative Thinking

I noticed the skin on my legs was dry and thought to myself that it was an inevitable part of ageing.

I forgot to buy some essential items while I was in the super-market and thought I must be getting old and forgetful.

I couldn't seem to thread a needle so I asked my son to do it and said: *My eyesight is not as good as it was, it must be my age.*

I had a late night and felt tired the next day, and now I re-member how often I told my partner: *I can't stay up late like I used to* and *I'm getting too old for late nights* and *I need my sleep at my age*; *I can't go to late-night parties anymore* and so on.

While out shopping I looked at the fashions and decided I was too old to wear those clothes any more, so I chose safe older clothes even though I know they make me feel and look older than I need to.

I am now aware of how often I think I shouldn't really do/wear this at my age.

New Thoughts

Examples of Positive Thinking

I can moisturize my skin daily, drink more water and keep my skin hydrated.

Even when I was 20 I forgot things; my memory is great and the odd slip-up has nothing to do with my age.

My eyesight is fine, and if I don't see something well I will blame the light or maybe being tired but I will never attribute it to my age. After all, at my grandmother's sewing circle she and her friends produce the most intricate stitching, so they must have good eyesight and they are all 80 years plus.

I can stay up late and have fun – it doesn't matter if I feel tired the next day. My children are tired all the next day if they stay up late and I never say they are getting too old for late nights since they are all under 10 years old.

I can adapt fashions and look stylish at any age. Dressing appropriately has more to do with my figure than my age, and I can wear leggings, a swimsuit or a modern outfit if I choose to.

I feel and look young, I believe I am young, so anything I want to do or wear suits me.

TO RECAP

Today on your first day you have learnt the absolute power of thoughts and how to change your thinking.

You now know that thoughts are things and that every single thought you have has a physical effect on your body and an emotional effect on your mind. All your thoughts have consequences – your healthy thoughts have healthy consequences, while negative thoughts will eventually have negative consequences.

All thoughts in the mind have to produce responses in the body, so by applying the techniques in this book and learning to accept only positive thoughts, ideas and beliefs about ageing you can programme your body to grow younger.

You have also learnt that your thoughts are yours to change, to update, to review and remove as they cease to be appropriate to you.

You have learnt how and why ageing cannot be defined and how you can redefine ageing in a positive way.

You have learnt how our lifespan is changing greatly.

You have also proved to yourself with the physical exercises the power of your thoughts on your body, and this will give you the proof and incentive you may need to take control of your thoughts rather than letting them control you.

Congratulations on taking your first step on the road to becoming *Forever Young*.

Thought For The Day
If you don't take control of your thinking someone else will.

Quote
What a marvellous thing is youth. What a pity it is wasted on the young.

GEORGE BERNARD SHAW

Imagination is more powerful than knowledge.

ALBERT EINSTEIN

Have you completed the exercises for Day One? If not, go back and complete them now. You can only move on to Day Two when you have fully completed Day One, as this is a process that is designed to change your thinking and ageing step by step. So you must complete each step systematically before moving on to the next one.

Changing Your Beliefs

You won't believe it when you see it.

You will see it when you believe it.

What we see and believe we become.

On Day One we have worked on your thinking. Now on Day Two it is time to work on your beliefs. *Aren't thoughts and beliefs the same thing?* I hear you saying. Well, no, they are not quite the same thing.

Many people think one thing and believe another, so their mind is in a form of conflict. If you want to age well it is very important that your thoughts and beliefs are congruent, that they match and go together so that they complement each other, especially if you want to grow younger.

If you can imagine thinking that you want to be wealthy while believing that rich people don't ever know who their friends are and that money brings problems, or thinking that you would love to get married while believing that marriages don't last, men/women are always unfaithful in the end, then you have examples of thoughts and beliefs being different and conflicting with each other.

A thought is something we hold in our minds, that we shape and form in our brain using language and pictures, whereas beliefs can be so silent yet immediate that we are not always aware they are even there, yet they are influencing us absolutely. For instance, if you believe that you are scared of dogs or birds your body will react to that belief as soon as you see a dog or a bird without you having to think about it at all. Your belief will set off an immediate reaction of fear within your body; it may react by having palpitations, shaking, sweating and even feeling sick. At the same time your thoughts may be busy saying: *It's only a little dog, it's on a lead, it can't harm me, it's far away*. But your thoughts alone are having little or no impact on your belief.

It is the same with our beliefs about ageing. We may not be aware of them, they are somewhat silent, but we react to them very strongly and they influence us twenty-four hours a day, which is why today you will be doing an exercise on uncovering beliefs. It may seem somewhat similar to the exercise you did yesterday but is in fact quite different.

We can change our thoughts quite easily with practice and repetition, but changing beliefs can take a little longer. The way to change a belief is to introduce doubt. If you have any beliefs you want to change, start to question where they originate from and why you are holding them and begin to introduce doubt as to their validity. As soon as you question a belief you are voicing doubt and no longer fully hold that belief to be true; the more you question a belief the more you doubt it.

This book will enable you to doubt and question much that you have been taught about ageing. As you doubt your old beliefs, your mind will be receptive and open to accept new beliefs that will have a much more beneficial effect on your ability to age differently and to stay young. It can sometimes take only seconds for a belief to change, which is one of the reasons detective stories with a twist in the tail are so popular – we believe one thing throughout and at the end our beliefs are challenged and changed.

Some universal examples of this are Rock Hudson, who was believed to be a sex symbol for women until it was discovered that he was gay; the film *Capricorn 1*, which caused many people to believe that a particular space mission was faked and staged in the desert; Lindy Chamberlain, who was believed for years to have killed her daughter until her baby's clothing was found in a dingo's den; babies switched at birth, and how that shakes up each parent's belief system, particularly when they have commented on traits that they feel are genetic and then discover their baby is genetically someone else's. Watergate was another example of almost a whole country having their belief system changed overnight.

Roger Bannister is a great example of this. It had been accepted and believed for centuries that a human could not run a mile in under four minutes, but Roger Bannister was determined to change this and he began by changing his own belief system. He saw the four minutes as 240 seconds, then repeatedly visualized himself running a mile in 239 seconds. And he did achieve this, using a form of self-hypnosis. He then changed the general belief system about this event because within a year a further thirty-seven runners ran a mile in under four minutes, followed the next year by 300 runners.

There are examples all around us of people who have held a belief to be true for years and then overnight their belief system has changed – people who have discovered they were adopted, or that their partner has been unfaithful, and of course positive examples as well, such as women who had been told they could not have children becoming pregnant, or people who didn't believe in God until something miraculous occurred that changed their belief immediately and permanently.

We used to believe the earth was flat, that a high-meat diet was healthy, that if you picked up a baby too much you would spoil it, all beliefs that have changed totally over the years. A whole generation of babies was brought up on beliefs that were later publicly denounced by the originator of the beliefs, who decided he was wrong. He ceased to believe his own beliefs with such conviction that he went on national television to apologize to a generation of mothers and to advise them to disregard everything he had taught. Many of these mothers had overridden their own nurturing instincts to kiss or pick up their infants because they believed he must be right; after all, he was an authority on children so they believed him.

As with thoughts, our beliefs are ours to change. Even definite, even rigid beliefs can be changed. In the area of ageing you have nothing to lose and everything to gain by deciding to continually assess and review your beliefs, and from now on to hold only beliefs about ageing that will be beneficial to you, that will empower you rather than disempower you.

There are different types and intensities of belief. There are beliefs that are opinions and beliefs that are convictions. Someone who is deeply religious would have a conviction, not open to doubt or change, since it would be stronger than an opinion, because in religion we are taught not to doubt but to accept without question the teachings of whichever religion we hold. Religion aside, I would ask you not to make your beliefs your jailer, to make them opinions rather than convictions so that you can change them, to be flexible in what you choose to believe rather than rigid and inflexible. Positive or negative thoughts can and will dictate our reality, and self-limiting beliefs can come true, whether based on fact or fiction.

We must challenge all negative beliefs about ageing, since they are not based on facts at all and are definitely not based on facts that are relevant to us. Many primitive tribes are completely free of the signs of ageing accepted as normal in the West. In certain areas of the world, including China, Japan, India the Hunza area of Pakistan, the Georgia area of Russia, Ecuador and parts of South America, people routinely live to be 100-plus and are very active. They still work, swim, exercise and are very involved in life. They have a very different belief system about ageing and are respected, revered and valued.

Ken Hom, the famous Chinese cook and author, says: *In China they believe you are nothing until you are 70; they value an older person's experiences because they can learn so much from them.* Since old age is looked up to in these cultures, people believe that as you grow older you grow in wisdom and esteem and consequently they look forward to getting older and see it as a welcome age, with many advantages and privileges to offer. Because of these different beliefs, they live longer healthier lives and look and feel much younger than they are.

Any changes you make in how you age must be preceded by a belief or thought that they will work or can work. Famous people and film stars are great examples for proving to us that what we have been led to believe about ageing can be contradicted. Sometimes when I am lecturing, people tell me that it isn't fair to use, say, Joan Collins as an example of being sexy at 60-plus, or Honor Blackman who is fabulous at 70, because of all the advantages someone in their position has. I completely understand this, yet there are many women out there who look just as fabulous and are doing it without the financial advantages of being a celebrity. I meet them all the time; however, since they aren't famous, we can't use them as examples. But they exist and are increasing in numbers almost daily. You can join them by using the techniques in this book.

When I was in the midst of writing this book, a participant at one of my lectures asked me: *How can we stop ageing; isn't it inevitable to age?* And I said: *Well, yes, in a way it is; from the moment we are born we are ageing and getting older, but rather than dispute that we age, the point is to question how we age and even why we age and what we believe about ageing.*

Some species, for example salmon, are programmed to age rapidly and then die very shortly after they have spawned, so really they only live long enough to procreate, whereas parrots and eagles have been shown to live for up to fifty years longer if they are removed from the elements, and the Galapagos tortoises can live for 200 years without any help. Humans are not programmed to age or die after procreation, since they can have children in their twenties and still be fit and active in their seventies.

Ageing may be inevitable, but the way we age is far from inevitable. After all, if you were to study a cross-section of 52-year-olds they would all be ageing quite differently and on their own timetable. If we included Goldie Hawn, Sally Field, Diana Ross and Lauren Hutton in that cross-section of people, we would have absolute proof that ageing as we think we know it is not inevitable. Before you say *Oh, but they are all an exception*, again I would ask you: *How do you know that they are not an example of normal ageing and it is everyone else that is an exception?* With every belief you have about ageing it is important to ask yourself, *Where did that belief come from? Where did I get that belief from and what authority did the person who held that belief have? Where did they get it from and is it relevant to me? Is it based on anything that is real and tangible?* You may surprise yourself with some of your answers.

Beliefs related to ageing are changing all the time. Thirty-five years ago it would have been unthinkable to have female sex symbols in their late thirties. Now it is accepted – in fact, in the last poll of Hollywood's most desirable women, Sharon Stone, Michele Pfeiffer, Madonna, Meryl Streep and Cher were in the top ten. Susan Sarandon looked wonderful collecting an Oscar at age 50, Felicity Kendall appeared naked on stage also at age 50, Catherine Deneuve and Lauren Hutton are modelling for major cosmetic and fashion companies in their fifties, and society has accepted this as no longer unusual. Julie Andrews looks very young at 60 and Lauren Bacall is full of energy at 72. Diana Ross and Susan Sarandon had babies in their mid- to late 40s. Even Thora Hird, at 80 years old, learning her lines so quickly and winning an award for her solo performance in *A Cream Cracker Under the Settee*, is an example to us that we don't have to lose our mental or physical agility at any age.

We can find an example to contradict every belief about ageing that exists. Barbara Cartland and Catherine Cookson continue to write more books every year and they are in their nineties – they have never allowed their age to stop them and they probably never will. If you have a reason to go on creating, to stay involved and active in life, your brain won't wither, since the brain does not wither with new things and our mind never ages. While most of us may have feared losing our agility and youth, would you dread ageing if you knew you would age like Katherine Hepburn, Martha Graham, Martha Gellhorn or Eileen Fowler?

Most statistics about ageing have been carried out on people who were hospitalized and had not aged well, but there are just as many examples of people who have aged excellently and even took up climbing or running marathons in their seventies. I'm not suggesting you need do that, but we can use these people as great examples, as role models.

- Artists Michelangelo and Picasso did amazing work in their nineties.
- Titian did his best work in his eighties and nineties.
- Verdi composed *Ave Maria* at 85.
- Martha Graham, the brilliant ballerina, was still performing on stage at 75 and at 95 was choreographing her 180th work.
- The pianist Horowitz played to a sold-out Carnegie Hall at 98.
- Arthur Rubenstein did the same at 90.
- Gladstone was prime minister at 85 and chopped trees daily.
- Oliver Wendell Holmes sat in the US Supreme Court in his nineties and said that faith in something keeps us young in spirit.
- Hulda Crooks began climbing mountains as she turned 70, and twenty-five years later made history when she became the oldest woman to climb Mount Fuji, which she did in her nineties.
- Tolstoy, Ormond McGill, George Burns, Katherine Hepburn, Katie Boyle, Gandhi, Golda Meir, Betty Boothroyd, Bette Davies, Mary Wesley, Michael Heseltine, Lou Grade, Jimmy Goldsmith . . . the list of people who retained their youth is endless.

If you lose the natural desire for discovery and adventure, the childlike drive to do new things, to build and create and grow, if you just drift along, you will experience ageing at any age.

We can and must keep finding attractive, exciting goals for the future. We may be tired of repetition – it doesn't mean we are tired of life.

You can be enthusiastic about life at any age, have goals that make you feel great about your future, about changing, have wide, varied interests, find things that allow you to feel excited about your future at any age and you won't grow old.

If you confront and change ideas that are not in harmony with youth, and instead become and stay active, alive and aware, you will remain young.

You can only grow old if you stop growing; your brain and body won't shrivel with new things and new situations.

George Bernard Shaw said: *Youth is wasted on the young.* You must believe that youth is a state of mind, know that your body doesn't really age and neither does your mind, and that you have the power to choose to stay young throughout your life and to look and feel young too.

Learn to welcome all the gains of maturity while remaining young, because you won't have lost anything unless you choose to believe that you have.

Society and the media have preached, to women especially, a very limited view of ageing, and lean towards worshipping youth and young bodies. Most of us would not even want to be back in our teens because they are often full of angst and insecurity. Teenagers have the highest suicide rate. But we do want to look and feel young. We can choose to love the security that comes with maturity, and believe that we look and feel better than ever and make that our reality.

Beliefs affect everything – our identity beliefs, which are beliefs that we hold to be true about ourselves, affect what we do, where we go, how we dress, how we live, and the friends and careers we choose. The most important beliefs are identity beliefs. They can be empowering or limiting, depending on how we formulate them, since the strongest force in humans is the need to remain consistent with how we define ourselves.

Never define yourself by how old you are in years or allow

anyone else to. Always define yourself positively, look at the ways you define yourself, notice the language you use when describing yourself and change any definitions that aren't positive. If you do this enough it becomes a way of life.

For example, Jill would believe:	*I look awful first thing in the morning.*
Sara would change that to:	*I wake up looking rested and refreshed and good.*
For example, Jill would believe:	*I look dreadful without make-up.*
Sara would change that to:	*Make-up makes me look even better.*

Beliefs actually create biology. There is nothing in the world more powerful than thought, no drug exists that is stronger than the mind. Beliefs are physical and real. Unfortunately, most people are completely unaware of the power of the mind. Unless you take charge of your thoughts and beliefs, you will be acting and reacting to beliefs fed to you by others which may have no relevance to you.

Since I want you to use the power of your mind to stay young, I am going to spend some of this chapter proving to you just how powerful your mind is, so that you can use it to slow down ageing, before I move on to show you how to use your mind consistently to look, feel and become younger.

By completing this very simple exercise you will be able to have an experience of how our beliefs cause physical changes to occur within our bodies.

Physical Exercise

EXERCISE 1

Stand up. Take one arm and, pointing your finger out in front of you, begin to turn your am as far out and behind you as you can. If it's your right arm move it out to the right, if it's your left move it out to the left. When you have moved your arm as far behind you as you can, notice where it is. Now return to the beginning position, close your eyes for a moment, and just imagine your arm moving even further up, to a third or 25 per cent further. Really see this in your mind for a moment, then open your eyes, repeat the procedure, and notice just how much further your arm will move.

You are already beginning to see the power of belief on the body. As you saw, believed and thought about your arm moving further, it did. Do it a few more times to prove to yourself how easy it is to influence our bodies using our belief system.

Athletes have been using this technique for years, seeing themselves lifting a heavier weight, performing a longer jump, believing they will do it, can do it and then doing exactly that. In fact, many tests have been done proving that in athletics the ability to visualize is as important as physical training.

When athletes visualize they can cause all their muscles to perform at a level to meet the visualization. It is now becoming accepted that in the future only athletes who use powers of visualization, as well as training, will succeed.

I recently made a television documentary with some of my clients who are Olympic athletes. They were talking about how many athletes at the last Olympic Games, from many different countries, used the power of thought, belief and visualization to succeed and how it gave them an advantage over those who didn't and helped them break world records.

You may have heard stories of people who are slightly built or unfit lifting a heavy object like a car, tree or refrigerator off their child, who is trapped underneath, and then wondering how they managed it. In fact they momentarily saw themselves performing the feat and then performed it because their mind, in that moment, believed they could and would do it.

Imagination is much more powerful than logic. You could cheerfully balance on a window ledge that was a few feet wide or walk along a plank of wood balanced on two blocks a few inches off the ground or placed on the carpet. However, should that window ledge or the plank of wood be 50 feet up or higher, the imagination may see you falling off and the belief that you might fall will be far more powerful than the knowledge that you can easily balance there.

One of the rules of the mind is that *Imagination is more powerful than logic.* Reason can be overruled by imagination, and you can use this to your advantage as you believe in becoming younger and then make it a reality.

People who have very strong religious beliefs are a good example of the power of the belief system. There are people who have willingly chosen to die because of their religious beliefs and believe that doing so is an honour. It is an important part of Japanese and Islamic culture.

The same examples apply with illness. People who see themselves as being ill, who believe they are ill, can and do manifest all the symptoms of illness, while people who refuse to see themselves as ill or who won't believe they are unwell frequently defy medical opinion. People who see themselves recovering, and use imagination to see cells being healthy and/or healing taking place, and who dwell on wellness not illness, recover much more, and more rapidly, than those who use the same powers of imagination and belief to see what is wrong with them.

Phantom pregnancy can be the most obvious example of thoughts/beliefs in the mind creating physical changes in the body. During a phantom pregnancy the breasts can produce milk, the stomach swells, and, should the phantom pregnancy continue to 'full term', labour can begin, with only some blood being passed. Dogs and horses often have phantom pregnancies.

Another fascinating example of the power of thought/belief on the body is with multiple personality disorder, where one personality may have allergies, need glasses or have arthritis, while another personality is completely free of them. Some female multiple personalities have even switched on and off their periods depending on which personality they are in at each moment.

These studies show us that cells are intelligent and make choices about how to behave below the level of our awareness. Cells have an intelligence of their own; every cell in your body has its own form of brain, and unlike your brain, which has learnt to doubt, and may doubt your intent when you say *I'm stopping smoking* or *I'm going on a diet today*, cells have no ability to doubt and believe everything we tell them and always will. If you constantly tell yourself you will remain young, that your cells are young, they will believe you and act accordingly.

You may come across people who scoff at what you are doing and say *I don't believe it*. When they do, just smile to yourself and remember that your cells absolutely believe it, your cells believe you. Your body believes it and is already acting accordingly, and that really is all that matters.

This book is for you to become younger. Don't try to make anyone else move over to your new point of view unless of course they want to. Other people may want to hold on to their old beliefs, which is their prerogative. The best way to influence people to change is to change yourself, so that they see the difference in you and want to follow.

Your cells, and your body, respond to what you believe, and beliefs change all the time, yet so many people condition themselves by believing things that are outdated and inappropriate. It used to be believed that having our teeth, appendix and tonsils removed as a matter of routine was beneficial, but now that belief has changed and we have been made aware it can be harmful to remove organs for no reason.

My grandmother, who was a beauty, had all her teeth removed when she was 30. She had migraines, and her doctor believed this drastic action (a widely held and accepted medical belief at the time) would cure her. When false teeth first appeared they were a status symbol, and many young wealthy people had all their teeth removed and replaced with false ones because of this belief.

So many beliefs based on medical opinions change, because medical opinions change, as new discoveries and facts come to light, and this is never more true than in the anti-ageing field. The belief that our bodies wear out in our sixties or seventies is false, and so is the belief that as we age everything goes into a decline.

Even the belief that our skin naturally begins to wrinkle and show signs of age from 30 years onwards is not true. Wrinkles don't actually need to appear before we are 60, and although genes and gravity are linked to their arrival, exposure to the sun is the real cause of wrinkles arriving prematurely. Only 10 per cent of ageing is natural or genetic – 90 per cent of wrinkles are caused by the sun. Wrinkles at 30 and 40 are a sign of sun damage, which accounts for 80–90 per cent of ageing and wrinkling, followed by the effects of smoking and pollution.

I had a client of 50 from Iran who had spent most of her life covered from head to foot in the *chadar*. Her skin had hardly ever been exposed to the sun, and she had no wrinkles and the skin of a 25-year-old. I am not suggesting we need to cover ourselves from head to toe to stay young, but to discount the belief that ageing is inevitable. In fact, our skin ages very slowly, even between the ages 20 to 60, but exposure to sun accelerates it.

Using a good sun block 365 days a year will also dramatically slow down the rate at which your skin ages. If you want to maintain young skin, always use a sunscreen with UVA/UVB filters, every day of the year, especially on the face, hands, neck, and the chest and breastbone, which has the thinnest skin on the body. It will work better if applied to damp skin. Use a sunblock with a Sun Protection Factor of at least 15 or even higher. Moisturizers and foundations or bronzers that contain their own SPF will not have a high enough factor, so use a sunscreen underneath. The Cancer Research Campaign does an excellent sun protection lotion with a SPF of 20, which was developed for Australia – all profits go to the Cancer Research Campaign.

If you want more proof of sun damage to exposed skin, compare the back of the wrist of your left arm with the skin on your inner right arm. Take your wrist or back of your hand and place it across your other arm at the inner arm near your armpit; compare the skin of the two different parts of the arms and notice how different the skin looks. Notice also how different the skin feels. The skin on your inner arm looks and feels younger than the skin on your hands. Pinch the skin on your inner arm between your thumb and forefinger, hold for five seconds, let it go, then count the number of seconds it takes for the skin to return to its previous condition. Do the same thing to the skin on your hand and you will see a big difference in the time it takes and how the skin pleats.

If this were because of ageing our skin would look the same all over our body. The skin on your inner arm is how all your skin would look and could look if it had not been damaged, because this skin gets protected from the sun whereas hands get the most exposure to the sun and can age ahead of us. A test done on middle-aged farming women from a village in Italy showed the exposed skin on their chests to be 30 years older than that on their inner arms. Sunscreen can prevent ageing spots on the hands, but you must wear it daily and reapply it every time you wash your hands.

The next major ageing factor is smoking, which ages skin by at the very least 10 per cent. Between the ages of 30 and 40 a smoker's skin will age by sixteen years. Smoking limits blood flow to our skin – it reduces the skin's ability to repair damage and causes an increase in free radicals. Puckering the mouth to draw on a cigarette causes deep mouth-to-nose lines and lines all around the mouth; squinting and half-closing the eyes during inhaling causes premature crow's feet, since our skin gets a memory when it is pleated or folded repeatedly and this memory is a wrinkle.

You can change your body by changing your beliefs; you can

quite definitely and visibly slow ageing down by removing pre-conditioned beliefs of ageing. We may have expected and learnt to age, but with all the new information available to us we can also expect and learn to slow ageing down, to age differently.

Bees are able completely to reverse their age hormonally when it is necessary for the hive. When there are not enough young bees to do the work that they are needed for, older bees will reverse their ageing, becoming younger and doing the work that is designated for young bees. If the hive moves or separates into two hives, the younger bees can become hormonally older and do the work of older bees. Therefore even bees have an awareness of ageing, and a proven ability to become younger.

Humans have the greatest awareness of ageing, and we can use this awareness to our advantage by deciding not to believe that ageing as we think we know it is inevitable, but instead to believe that we can positively influence how we age, not just now but for all our lives.

Mental Exercise

EXERCISE 1

It is very important that you stop and think about your beliefs and how they are related to how you are ageing. In fact, over the next few days and weeks become aware of any self-limiting beliefs you hold regarding ageing and remember, they exist only in your imagination, since we can always find examples to counteract these beliefs.

Begin to root out and eradicate these beliefs and replace them with more positive beliefs. The mind can only hold one thought at a time, so you can banish negative beliefs and replace them with positive ones, once you have identified them and their origin and realized you can choose what to believe or not. Just because something was held to be true by a relative, it does not have to be true for you.

Find a quiet moment, close your eyes and begin to recall

your parents' and your grandparents' attitudes and beliefs about ageing. Keep your eyes closed and really go into this – allow yourself to uncover all the silent hidden beliefs that have been affecting you. Include neighbours, teachers, employers.

Did they focus a lot on being too old to do things any more?

Did they retire and spend long periods of time in a chair or inactive?

Did they dress or act older before they needed to and was their language all directed to getting older?

If they did, then it's important for you to know that we all have 25,000 hours of conditioning fed to us by parents and other influential figures which is constantly being played back to us. You must begin to change your dialogue, change the beliefs about ageing fed to you by others.

What about your friends' beliefs – do they match your own? Do you go along with what they have said just because they said it? Close your eyes and just allow yourself to hear all the things you have heard from your family and your friends about ageing.

Use your diary or notebook to write out the attitudes and beliefs about ageing of people who could have influenced you and which you are now ready to see as outdated. Write out each person's name and their beliefs.

Underneath each attitude or belief write out something new, positive and appropriate to you. Copy this list of new beliefs and keep it nearby or pin it up. Look at it and repeat these new beliefs to yourself daily.

Example: *My mother always told me that getting older meant getting fatter and out of shape.*

Change to: *I don't have my mother's body and I maintain a fit healthy body at every stage of life.*

Example: *My grandmother believed that everything ached with age and exercise was bad for old people.*

Change to: *Chinese people practise t'ai chi at all ages and exercise has never been bad for them.*

Example: *My employer/boss believed that younger employees are more productive.*

Change to: *Older employees are more dedicated and reliable.*

Example: *My father used to say 'Mutton dressed as lamb' about our neighbour who always dressed young, so I feel uncomfortable about being ridiculed if I wear young fashions.*

Change to: *Perhaps he envied her. Keeping up to date with some current fashions allows me to feel and look younger.*

Example: *My grandparents believed that old people need lots of rest. I seem to remember them always sitting in the same armchair and being inactive.*

Change to: *I have learnt through this book that our bodies do not wear out with age. Inactivity accelerates ageing. I loved my grandparents but they were misinformed and wrong.*

Now decide what you are going to think about age in relation to yourself. Write out these new beliefs on a new page and adopt them, accept them as your beliefs from now on.

Remember that you can succeed or fail in your ability to remain young,

Depending on:

what you choose to believe,

what you choose to hold in your mind as true or not true,

what you choose to see as relevant to you or irrelevant to you.

You may find as you go through Day Two's written exercises that they seem very similar to those of Day One. In Day One you are discovering and confronting your own thoughts about ageing, whereas in Day Two you are discovering and confronting the beliefs about ageing passed on to you by other people. Some of these may be the same or very similar, but even if you find yourself writing out some things that are the same as Day One, keep going, because it is important to release every negative thought and belief before you move on to Day Three. Through these exercises you can analyse where this belief came from, how you got it and why you believe it.

TO RECAP

Today, on Day Two, you are already a fifth of the way through the programme and changes will have begun to take place within you.

Today you have learnt that something we may have held to be true for years may be just an outdated belief, especially in the area of ageing.

You have learnt that there are different types of beliefs and to change any belief we need to introduce doubt, because when we question and doubt a belief we no longer really hold it to be true.

You have seen how examples of people who are living long, full and youthful lives are able to change our beliefs.

Well done for another day of taking action to move towards becoming *Forever Young*.

Thought For The Day
Unless you direct your mind it will direct you.

Quote
Man is what be believes.

ANTON CHEKHOV

Man's mind stretched to a new idea never goes back to its original dimensions.

OLIVER WENDELL HOLMES

Remember, before you can move on to Day Three you must have completed all the exercises of Day Two. If you haven't completed them, go ahead and complete them now before you move on to Day Three.

DAY 3

Changing Your Language

Today, on Day Three, we are going to look at the power of language.

Language and the words we use associated with ageing have a very powerful effect on the body and mind – words have an emotional content, and what we associate with the words we use shapes how we feel about things. Experiments have been done showing that if we take on someone else's emotional vocabulary we also take on their emotional state, so don't take on or use the language of someone else unless you want to be like them.

Notice how people who have not aged well complain or draw attention to their age or aches and pains all the time, while those who have aged well tend to draw attention to how well they feel. Eliminate words like *tired*, *exhausted*, *worn out*, *shattered*, *depressed*, *sick*, because the label or word you use to describe how you feel becomes how you feel. Our mind responds to words that are descriptive because it makes its work easier to do, so use only descriptive words that are positive.

Since words are the structure of our reality, it follows that if we change our words then we change our reality. Certainly making changes in the language we use alters very quickly how we feel. It is so important to pay attention to our thoughts and language connected with ageing.

Our cells listen and react to our language. Let's imagine that Jill might say *I'm too old to go to aerobic classes any more; it's too exhausting for me.* Immediately her mind and body will accept this as a fact and, believing she is too old, will cause her to feel and act older than she needs to. However, making a very simple change to her language and saying *I'm too tired to go to aerobics today so I will take it easy and go tomorrow* will have a very different effect on her body. Instead of saying *I look old*, Sara would decide to say *I look a little stressed*. Instead of saying *I am exhausted or worn out*, Sara would say *I need to enjoy some deep sleep so that I can look refreshed and relaxed*.

If you use ageing language, and if your image of yourself is old or ageing, then your inner intelligence will pass on through each cell generation the belief that you are old or ageing.

The same is true with weight and addictions. If your language and thoughts are all along the lines of, *I can't lose weight, I can't eat like other people do*, then you are passing on that information from one cell to the next. Cells are not able to disagree with you and accept everything you say and even think as a fact, so you have nothing to lose and everything to gain by telling yourself and your cells the opposite. Tell yourself you look and feel ageless.

I have noticed that even small children see the word *old* as negative. I bought my 5-year-old daughter an antique doll's house and when I showed it to people I would say *It's very old* or *It's 100 years old*. My daughter was really far too young to have been given it and would either try to get inside it or swing on the doors as they opened out. I must have said to her *Don't do that, because this doll's house is very old* too many times, because one day she said to me, *Mummy why don't we get rid of that doll's house — it is so old — and get a pink Barbie house instead?*

That got me thinking about where she could have picked up the belief that old equals undesirable. I noticed my language — I said things like *Throw away that stuff in the fridge, it's really old*, or *Don't drink that, it's old*, or when clearing out her room I would say *Do you want to keep all these old things or could we get rid of some of them?* And of course she hears me talk to other people – I might say to my partner *Don't wear that, it looks so old*, or *I need some new training shoes, these are old now*, or *This item is getting old, we have to replace it*.

People value newness so much, especially children, who love having new things. Yet some of my favourite things are my oldest things, and my daughter certainly loves her oldest teddy bear the best. I now endeavour not to equate undesirable things with their age, and say *Don't eat that, it isn't fresh* or *It's gone off, it's stale* or *mouldy* rather than saying it is old.

If you think about the context in which you use the word *old* it may give you some insight into why so many people dread ageing. We value special objects that are old, yet we also use the word *old* as a prefix for replacing something or discarding something believing it no longer has any value.

In the area of language the mind reacts very badly to the word *loss*, so if you mourn your lost youth and believe that your schooldays were the best days of your life, if you use expressions like *It's all downhill from now on* or *I am losing my looks*, again you will accelerate the ageing process. With weight loss, focusing on the word *loss* does not work. The greatest human pain is all to do with what we believe we have lost. When people talk about losing weight they frequently gain it back and then view the weight gain with horror. *Gain* is a positive word, *loss* is negative, so change your vocabulary and focus on gaining a slim figure or gaining energy, vitality and a feeling of youthfulness. Always focus on feeling young and losing the old beliefs that have been so detrimental to you. Focus on maintaining a youthful attitude and approach to life at any age, and on gaining more knowledge, ability and the desire to look after your body and your health.

Physical Exercise

EXERCISE 1
I am old and weak *v.* I am young and vibrant

You need someone to help you do this. Make a fist and make one arm as strong and rigid as you can. Hold that arm out in front of you and get your helper to push down on that arm to test your strength, while you use all your strength to resist them.

Now you have established your strength, think of the most negative words or beliefs you use about yourself in relation to ageing. Repeat these words out loud ten times or just think them silently, ten times. An example could be *I am old and weak* or *I am constantly getting older and less desirable.* Now, thinking these thoughts, make your arm strong again and repeat the strength-testing process. You will find your strength has diminished. Amazing, isn't it! As you think those negative thoughts you are losing all the strength in your muscles and your arm is becoming weak. This is more proof of the amazing powers of the mind.

Would you like more proof of the powers of thought, language and belief on the body? Proof that thought or belief is more powerful than effort in tests of strength? This time think of some positive thoughts about ageing yet remaining young, and repeat them silently or out loud ten times.

If, like many of us, you have been led to believe that there is nothing positive about ageing, then repeat this ten times: *I am remaining young, healthy and vibrant, my body and mind are always young.* Now, thinking these thoughts, make your arm strong again and repeat the strength-testing process. Isn't it great to see that as you think positive thoughts you become physically stronger? I mentioned earlier that every thought you have creates a physical reaction in the body and you have just proved it to yourself.

Where a thought goes, energy goes with it; so you see,

changing your thinking and using different language really does change your body.

Most people are fascinated by this testing, and since it is a fun thing to do I recommend you spend some time playing with it.

Repeating all the negative thoughts and beliefs you have.
Using all the negative words you had been using before realizing the power of language.
Testing your strength.
Replacing these beliefs with positive constructive beliefs.
Testing your strength again and seeing the difference.

You can do this with so many beliefs, not only in the area of ageing but in beliefs you have about your confidence, self-esteem, weight, habits, abilities, relationships – in fact anything at all.

Remember, these beliefs only exist in your imagination and you are free to change your thinking and your language as soon as you become aware of how limiting and destructive your language and beliefs are. After all, your thoughts are yours to change, your mind is yours to direct, and your beliefs and language are yours to alter.

While the mind does run the body, it is your mind and you are able to direct it, to change it, and to influence positive changes in yourself. Changing your language is one of the quickest ways to do this.

Mental Exercise

EXERCISE 1

Think of all the words and language you use to describe yourself. Write out all the words on a fresh page of your workbook, then go through them deleting words that are not positive. As you delete them you can replace each word with a new and more appropriate word, or you can just erase those words from your vocabulary without needing to replace them.

Examples: *old, too old, ancient, antique, over the hill, past it, gaga, wrinkly, exhausted, worn out, shattered, depressed.*

Delete all these words and/or find new words to replace them.

Never say *God, I look ancient* or *I feel ancient*, even in jest, and don't use words like *geriatric, antique, past it, over the hill, gaga, past my sell-by date.*

You can retain a youthful skin and body through the power of your mind, but you won't if you keep using awful words like *past it, over the hill, no spring chicken, old boiler, old fogey* to describe yourself, even if it's only jokingly. Remember, our subconscious mind has no sense of humour and takes everything we say literally.

It's vital to laugh and to have a sense of humour and it's OK to make fun of yourself, but not in the area of your age.

Most people only joke about ageing because they feel uncomfortable about it.

I find language a fascinating subject. There are 750,000 words in the English language and most people only use 1,200 of them. And most people have the same twelve words that they use to describe their experiences and feelings. It is especially interesting to me that many people use very descriptive and powerful words to describe events that are mediocre, and use words that are not powerful enough to describe good things that are happening to them.

Sometimes a patient will arrive at my office and say *I've had a hellish morning on the M25* or *The parking around here is a nightmare* or *I've been stuck in the supermarket, it's bedlam in there* or even *I've had the most tortuous time getting here.* Then just for good measure they will add *My back is killing me* or *I have starved myself all week but I still look as fat as a house.*

Without realizing it, they are using very powerful, descriptive words to describe events that aren't really that important and need to be forgotten, not elevated and remembered in the mind as scenes of hell, bedlam, torture, or a nightmare.

Describing pain as *killing* can only intensify the pain. Saying you are *ravenous* or *starved* will cause you to over-eat, because your mind will believe you are starved and will shut down your appetite control mechanism which knows how much you eat and tells you when you have had enough.

Saying *I look enormous*, *I'm as big as a house*, *as fat as a pig* gives the mind a very clear image to take you to.

When these same clients begin to talk about good events in their life or how they are feeling, they use words that are weak or not descriptive, like: *It was quite good, It was OK really, I had a nice time, It was fun, We had a laugh, It turned out all right, I'm not too bad, I'm OK, I'm all right, I'm fine*. These words are so un-descriptive, so vague and wishy-washy that they fail to have an impact on the mind.

If you want to feel better, use words that are very descriptive, that make a picture, that are thrilling or exciting and powerful.

Even the words you place in front of words will have an effect on how you feel. This is especially true with swear words, which are used to intensify a feeling. If you say *It was awful* but add in front of that it was *absolutely awful*, *bloody awful*, *positively awful* or *absolutely bloody awful*, you get a stronger response in your mind and body to how awful it was and to how awful you feel it was.

If you say *It was amazing*, then add *truly amazing*, *simply amazing*, *absolutely amazing*, you again get a stronger reaction to the event – only this reaction is positive, the previous one negative.

If you describe yourself as *a pig*, then put in front of it *I'm a big fat pig*, your mind creates a much more vivid picture and a more intensified feeling accompanies those words.

★

I would like you to think of the words you use the most frequently, both positive and negative, to describe your feelings or to describe yourself. Write the positive words in the left-hand column and the negative in the right, and now increase the positive words and decrease the negative words.

Do this by writing down the words and even the sentences you use most frequently to describe yourself in two opposite pages of your workbook, or divide a page into two columns, one headed *positive* and the other headed *negative*. Minimize the negative and accentuate the positive.

Example:

POSITIVE	NEGATIVE
I am not bad-looking.	*I have frown lines.*
This is not positive enough – change and accentuate to:	This is negative – minimize it to:
I look wonderful.	**They are character lines and tiny.**
I am not bad for my age.	*I get tired more often.*
This is not positive enough – change and accentuate to:	This is negative – minimize it to:
I am an excellent example of ageless ageing.	**I rest more and then have abundant energy.**

Now think of the words you use in front of words and decide to put words like *absolutely*, *definitely*, *positively*, *unquestionably*, and so on in front of your new positive statements.

Use words of a different intensity, like *slightly*, *mildly*, *occasionally*, and so on, in front of negative statements.

Don't use words with a strong, negative, emotional content;

don't say things like *I am dreading being 50* or *I can't bear to think of being a pensioner* or *I loathe the thought of old age*, because the more descriptive and negative those words are the more they will elevate in a negative way how you feel about ageing when it could be a wonderful time of life.

An example of this is to change *I have a throbbing, pounding pain* to *I have a slight pain*. If you are used to saying *I have horrible wrinkles all over my body*, change it to *I have a very slight amount of wrinkling in certain parts of my body*.

What our mind sees it believes without question. The mind has no capacity to reason – it believes whatever we tell it, so get into the habit of telling yourself positive things only. Also get into the habit of being very aware of the words you use to describe things, and most especially to describe yourself, because your mind particularly responds to words and images that are symbolic. The subconscious mind loves descriptive words.

If you say *I'm an antique* or *I'm ancient* your mind first makes a picture of what that means, then works to have you feel and act in ways that match the pictures you are causing your mind to make. If you say *I have a raging headache* or *I have a crippling stomach pain* your body works to meet the mind's description. Simply changing that to *I have a mild pain in my head* or *I have a slight ache in my stomach* brings about completely different sensations.

When I hypnotize clients who are giving birth I remove the words *labour*, *pain* and *contractions* from the conditioning tape I make for them, and talk instead about *delivery*, *birth signals*, *rushes*, *feelings*, *sensations*, *euphoria*. Many of my clients who listen to this tape during the last stages of pregnancy and during delivery say they love it, because it contains no negative words and allows them to experience childbirth in a more manageable way.

When I was pregnant I was amazed that my ante-natal clinic wanted to remind me at every visit to be prepared for post-natal depression. I would always reply: *I am going to have post-natal euphoria*. Eventually I stopped going to the clinic because they always seemed to talk about the pain of birth, the baby blues and the exhaustion of being a new mother. I had a very easy pregnancy and birth and I *did* have post-natal euphoria – I was on a high after my baby was born and I had so much energy. Some of this was natural and a lot of it was to do with the fact that I had conditioned myself to believe different things. I used different language and thought different thoughts. I had great motivation to do this, since I went on live television three weeks after my baby's birth to demonstrate hypnosis for childbirth on a pregnant lady who was phobic about hospitals. And I took my baby on the programme with me.

I was regarded as somewhat of an exception because I returned to my normal weight in a week and felt fantastic. I still believe that a lot of the things we hear about pregnancy – the weight that takes a year to go, the tiredness, the depression – can also be negative conditioning that many women react to automatically because of the way the mind works.

You may need to persist with changing your language and vocabulary if you have been using powerful words to describe sensations for some time. The mind learns by repetition, and by a new process of positive repetitions, using much better language, you will see and experience definite changes.

Using this book and these examples will show you how to

- take control of how you age
- challenge beliefs about ageing
- re-create your thoughts and beliefs re ageing
- change your attitudes, assumptions, awareness and language connected to ageing
- commit to feeling young and living a young life

Take control, as opposed to being helpless and letting ageing just happen to you.

Take charge, rather than giving up and expecting a decline into ageing.

Most people only fear and resist change in case they become worse off.

We don't have to dread ageing because changing years is not ageing.

This book will help you take control of the direction of ageing and ensure that the direction of all change is towards improvement so that you can feel good about yourself. It is actually very hard to feel good about ourselves unless we feel that we are influencing the direction of change in our lives.

I could write a complete book on my experiences with clients who change their thoughts and beliefs and create wonderful changes within themselves, but I will describe just a few.

Mrs D., a delightful American lady, came to see me while she was in England for a few weeks. She had been trying to get pregnant for thirteen years, and had done almost everything, including many attempts at IVF. Eventually she gave up and was able to arrange a private adoption with a young single mother who was pregnant. She was in London a month before the birth was due, and came to see me to use hypnosis for confidence.

Obviously she was very excited about the baby. She would arrive at my office with all kinds of baby clothes and toys which she had waited thirteen years to buy, and would show me her purchases while we talked about her impending motherhood. Her joy and delight were contagious. While in London she received a phone call informing her that the baby had been born one month early and the mother could not bear to part with her.

Mrs D. was devastated. She stayed on in England for a few extra weeks, feeling unable to return to her home, where the baby's room was waiting, and we worked through these feelings. She then returned to America determined to keep going and eventually adopt another baby. Five weeks after her return she called me to say that she was pregnant, had been pregnant while in England but had had no idea. To everyone this seemed the most wonderful miracle. While she was focusing on being a mother-to-be, on becoming a mother, she got pregnant and at last had her baby.

Many women who want children focus on why they can't get pregnant and say things like: *Why can't I have a baby? What's wrong with me?* They hope, wish and pray for motherhood, which is so understandable.

Mrs D., unaware of what she was doing, actually focused on being a mother. She talked about her baby, shopped for her baby, and completely accepted herself as a mother.

She saw herself as a mother rather than wishing, hoping and longing to become one.

Couples who have adopted have sometimes become pregnant, and it has been said that this is because they have relaxed about the whole issue once they have got their baby through adoption. I believe it's because unquestionably they saw themselves and accepted themselves as parents.

If there is something that you want, don't wish, hope, long for, or dream of it, see it as if you already have it, believe it is happening for you now, since the mind only works in the present tense. Know that it will happen.

When you wish for something, you send a message to the brain that says *I want this but I don't believe I can ever have it.* When you say *I will try*, your brain immediately accepts the word *try* as so insignificant that it does not matter if you get the results or not – when you say *I will* instead you get a very different and positive response.

Saying *I hope it works* allows your mind to believe that you doubt it will work. Saying *I dream about* is interpreted by the mind as dreaming about something because you have already accepted it is not attainable or not going to happen.

Some years ago I was asked to work with a little boy who had eczema. His parents were very keen that he might find a cure, while his grandmother, who lived with the family, would comment frequently that they should all stop fussing since it would go away when he started school. I could not give them an appointment until after he had begun his first term at school, as I was very busy. Interestingly, as soon as he began school the eczema started to diminish and by the time he arrived for his appointment it had already improved by 75 per cent because he had accepted his grandmother's words and his mind had acted upon them.

Occasionally clients book appointments to stop smoking or nailbiting and arrive for the said appointment having already stopped or considerably reduced the habit because they expected to and in a sense saw it happening.

I have my own personal experience of the power of thought. Having been told I couldn't have children, I went on to get pregnant very easily, helped by the fact that I did not ever accept the fact that I would be childless. Now I have a wonderful daughter. I used hypnosis throughout my pregnancy and had the easiest pregnancy, an easy birth and a baby who was so content and hardly every cried.

I was put on thyroid medication for years and told I could never come off it and could not get pregnant on or off it, but I became pregnant and decided after my daughter's birth not to take any more medication. With the help of a wonderful doctor who believed I did not need the medication, I came off it easily and have never felt better.

Last year I went on a course in Hawaii that involved walking on burning coals and climbing 50-foot telegraph poles. Before I left England I decided that I would pass on the pole climbing – I stood on the roof of a building that was 50 feet high and didn't like it very much. I noticed that I was saying to myself *I'm not going to climb the pole*. When I arrived in Maui and saw other people climbing the poles, I declined – I told people that I didn't want to do it and had no intention of doing it. On my last but one day, I watched a little girl of 5 climb the pole and this immediately changed my thinking. I decided if she could do it so could I.

As I changed my thinking, everything changed: I began to want to do the climb, I started to feel excited about it. A few hours later I was standing on top of the pole balancing on one leg, having my photograph taken. It was wonderful and thrilling; I loved every moment of it and it was a wonderful lesson to me on changing my thinking and my feelings. I will always be grateful to that little girl, Diana – thank you.

After that the fire walking was easy. A few years ago I would never have gone on the course, but I'm so glad I did, as it opened my eyes even more to the wondrous power of the mind over the body.

TO RECAP

Today, on Day Three, you have learnt the power of language, the very real and physical effects of the spoken word and of your language both on your mind processes and on your self.

You are almost a third of the way through the book, and are already well on the way to noticing changes beginning to occur in how you feel and how you look.

You are well into the programme and steadily moving through it. You will have already achieved so much just by completing this third day, and you have so much more to achieve. I hope you are enjoying it and finding making these changes fascinating, fun and compelling.

Thought For The Day
As you speak you are. As you continue to speak so you remain.

Quote
Words form the thread on which we string our experiences.

ALDOUS HUXLEY

PART TWO

Understanding

DAY **4**

Changing Your Physiology

Today, on Day Four, we are moving on to a new section of the book, leaving the preparation section and moving on to the understanding section. The next three chapters and the next three steps involve showing you how your mind works and how you have the ability to influence it beneficially. Your mind absolutely influences your body, but it is *your* mind and you have the power to direct it and influence it in the most positive way.

Today you are going to learn how to make your body feel younger because, as you know by now, this will actually lead your body to becoming younger. Having your body feel younger and consequently become younger is very easy to do, and you only need to spend a few minutes daily, or 10–15 minutes three or four times a week, to get the desired results and to keep them.

Your muscles have a memory which can be activated by your beliefs and by your physiology – you never forget how to ride a bicycle because it is in your physiology. Doing things you did when younger not only reminds your muscles of how to behave and what to do, but also reminds your cells that this is the activity of a youngster and as we participate in it our cells feel, act and ultimately behave younger. Swimming, skipping and trampolining are excellent examples of activities that have this effect on our cells. Cycling also works if you activate memories of being a child while cycling for fun – riding an exercise bike in the gym won't have the same effect.

You will read later how important exercise is in remaining young, but taking exercise to remain fit and supple and to have stronger bones is not what we are talking about here. Even if you already take regular exercise, in the form of running, weight training or anything else that excludes the activities mentioned in the previous paragraph, you still need to participate in other activities that are designed to make you feel young rather than to give your body a work-out.

There are some activities, like swimming, jumping, skipping, that do both, but when you engage in these in order to keep fit they usually take an hour or so and lose their spontaneous fun aspect over extended periods of time. This isn't to say we don't enjoy them, but they can become competitive as well. Keep exercising for the benefit of keeping fit separate from moving in a childlike way in order to become biologically younger.

I enjoy working out most of the time, but I separate that from the times when I dance around or jump up and down. When I do it with my daughter it is even more fun. To exercise or work out regularly will cause you to become young biologically because of the physical effect it has on your body and organs. To participate in young activities that are fun will cause you to feel young, and this is transmitted to your organs and causes you to become physically younger.

Trampolining regularly for 10–20 minutes three or four times a week is an important step in anti-ageing. It is excellent for cells and age reversal because it stimulates our production of lymph, which is essential for looking and feeling healthy. We have more lymph in our body than we have blood; however, the lymph does not have a pump and relies on us taking deep diaphragmatic breaths and moving a lot to allow the lymph to move around the body. Muscle movement and gravity are meant to keep lymph flowing, pump lymph back through its channels, and eliminate waste. Running, trampolining, jumping, skipping, swimming and other forms of aerobic exercise encourage correct lymph activity and flush wastes from tissue fluids.

Using a mini-trampoline for just a few minutes daily is excellent for promoting correct lymph movement. We eliminate waste through our skin, lungs, kidneys and colon. Up to a third of waste elimination is through the skin – our sweat glands are meant to expel a minimum of 1 lb of waste material daily. When they don't, because our bodies are not working at peak efficiency, this toxic waste can remain in our system causing all kinds of damage and accelerating ageing. Trampolining changes the force of gravity in the body.

James White, an exercise physiologist in California, put half of a group of previously inactive older women on a trampolining programme and noted that those on the trampolines looked younger than the group that remained inactive. Their skin tone and colouring improved, wrinkles diminished, and so, to his amazement, did the bags under their eyes. These changes occurred rapidly. The intense rhythmic pressure stimulates cells to release waste.

Another benefit is that because while bouncing on a trampoline to some fun music we feel like children, we are feeling young psychologically, and this will make us younger biologically. You can buy mini-trampolines for less than £20 in many sports shops. As you bounce, think positive thoughts, say the affirmations you will learn about on Day Five, and repeat your new beliefs, since they will go directly into your subconscious mind and influence you in the most perfect way.

Ensure that you rebound correctly and safely, with heels pushing down into the trampoline every time you bounce down on to it. If you don't have a trampoline and don't want to buy one, jumping or skipping or playing hopscotch are all excellent. Swimming is perfect, because the combined action of water and muscle movement stimulates the lymphatic system. It is as good as trampolining, and better for people who have joint, weight or heart problems.

If for any reason you can't engage in any kind of physical

activity, there are other ways your body can become younger, such as giggling and laughing out loud. Even playing board or card games from your past can evoke feelings of youth and have the desired effect of ultimately making you younger.

Moving around to some music that we particularly like is equally good for making our bodies believe they are younger. Music can instantly take us back to our past – the music that was played on our first date, at our first dance, or the music we fell in love to. Needless to say, you should only play music that evokes happy memories.

Find recordings of songs that have the word *young* in them and make a point of playing them daily. Set aside a few minutes and dance to them every day – it will make you feel great. Any fun music or rhythmic music that you love will do the same, but if you listen to some of the songs listed below, if you play them over and over, you will find that the lyrics become embedded in your mind. The combination of words and music will bypass the conscious and put the message straight into your subconscious, enabling you to use appropriate lyrics as affirmations, hearing the positive messages they contain being played back to you again and again. You can even sing them out loud – you will be taking another positive step to feeling and becoming younger.

'Young at Heart' by Frank Sinatra
'Young at Heart' by The Bluebells
'You Make Me Feel So Young' by Frank Sinatra
'Forever Young' by Bob Dylan and also by Chrissie Hynde
'Young Turks, Young Hearts, Be Free Tonight' by Rod Stewart
'Young, Gifted and Black' by Bob and Marcia
'When You're Young and in Love' by The Marvelettes

If you know of any other titles with the word *young* or the theme of youth in them, please write to me and let me know what they are, as I play these songs during the breaks at my seminars and love having more titles to use.

When we fall in love we become very childlike. Falling in love is an act of regression, so we act much more like children. We become spontaneous and carefree, we touch and explore, rub noses, talk in baby talk, find pleasure in the most simple things, and notice that time stands still and that we become absorbed and focused on one thing, oblivious to all else. These are all qualities that children have. We dance around and smile a lot even at total strangers, we laugh more, we sing to ourselves and feel content, and while we are doing this our bodies are growing younger. Falling in love can make us become younger, and it makes us look visibly better.

Now you may not be in a position to fall in love just like that, but you can put yourself in a position of recreating the feelings. Remember how it felt to be in love, and recreate some or all of those feelings. Children seem to be in love with life – they can find pleasure in rain, wind, in a puddle, a rainbow, in anything. We can learn a lot by remembering that we once had all those qualities and it is never too late to reclaim them. As we grow up we get wrinkles, but the worst place to have wrinkles is in your enthusiasm.

Children are naturally spontaneous, creative and flexible. When I was taking my daughter to school I noticed a large puddle in the playground. Most of the mothers were saying, *Don't go near that puddle, don't get your feet wet*, and one little boy ran up with glee straight into the puddle, where he happily splashed about, soaking his shoes and socks, while his mother looked on exasperated. When children come across puddles they jump in; when adults come across them they moan and complain about them. Sometimes we need to be childlike and jump in the puddle as well.

As I was walking down my street with my daughter, she said, *Mummy, I've never seen you run or skip along this road – please skip with me.* So because it was important to her, and I was in a carefree mood, I took her hand and skipped along the road with her, feeling a bit foolish. I was doing this solely for her, but noticed after a few minutes how good it felt. We were giggling and laughing, and I felt so young and childlike, and of course being in this business I knew what a great effect this was having on my cells and on my psychological and biological age. I vowed to do it more often.

There are other times when I have no desire to do this, when I don't want to be in the park, or playing, and I want to be serious and adult. It is all to do with being appropriate: do childlike things when you can, but don't wait for the mood to hit you − make it happen as well. Whenever I've hired a bouncy castle for my daughter's birthday the adults can't wait to have a go on it once the children are elsewhere. There is something about that party environment, the balloons, the children's food and giggling, the clown entertainer, the music, that carnival-like atmosphere, that make us regress back to childhood for a few delightful moments. I believe we should be encouraged to do this more, not less, because of the positive effect it has on our cells.

Khalil Gibran wrote, in 1899: *You may strive to be like your children but seek not to make them like you.* So if your husband is playing with the train set or flying his son's kite don't laugh at him, laugh with him. Play on a pogo-stick, trampoline together and feel young, and then, when you stop, notice that tingling all over your body − it is the life force, the energy of your cells feeling revitalized.

I am aware that many parents reading this won't agree with me, and I've been to enough children's parties where the hosts feel they are too busy making the day a success to play and find the event stressful. Still, we can always take just a few minutes to enjoy ourselves too, especially since it will result in us look-ing and feeling younger.

At my daughter's first birthday party I was so busy doing things that I forgot to take a single photograph of the happy day. Since then I have made a point of enjoying myself. I also went to a good friend's wedding and found her in tears − she was so busy trying to make everything just right and perfect for everyone else that she felt it was not her day any longer and she was not having fun at all. On what was meant to be one of the happiest days of her life, she was feeling stressed, tense and miserable. I have done that in the past – spent so long organizing a party or dinner and then not enjoyed it, had no fun, the whole point of giving the party in the first place.

It is never too late to be young and childlike, and never too late to have a happy childhood. If you did not do these things as a child, then that is even more reason to do them now. Women like Felicity Kendall, Sally Field and Goldie Hawn are good examples of this because they have that young, girlish attitude, the giggle and body language of a child which keeps them young. Even Barbara Cartland believes she is young, which has a very positive effect on her.

You are discovering that you have the power to make your body become younger. You also have the power to make your mind become younger and to stay mentally young throughout your life. The brain is a very self-rejuvenating organ but, like the body, it has to be used regularly in order to work at its best. By regularly stimulating your brain you can maintain mental agility into your nineties and beyond.

Just as you need to exercise your body to maintain its strength and agility, you need to keep doing mental exercise to stay young. Tests on university professors aged 60–74 found that they were as accurate on memory and mental tests as younger people, and far better than those who shared their age, because they had stayed intellectually active. Even tests on animals who are kept stimulated show that the neurons in their brains remain strong and continue to renew themselves, whereas they wither when the same animals are not kept in stimulating surroundings.

If you continue to work your brain by participating in any of the following activities, you will use and stretch your mental faculties. Practice and skill will keep your mind young, and this will influence your body to remain young too.

Crossword puzzles are a very good form of giving the brain a workout. Other mental exercises to keep your brain in good shape and your mind young are:

- Reading and keeping up with current affairs
- Memorizing poems, facts and articles
- Playing chess, draughts and word puzzles
- Joining in radio and television quiz shows, competing with the contestants to answer questions
- Participating in magazine and newspaper competitions, brain teasers and other mind activities
- Learning something new – a language, a musical instrument, performing in amateur dramatics, learning lines

You can even train your eyes to work better and to stay younger by beading or threading a string.

Let's go back to Jill and Sara:

Jill would stop herself dancing around to music. She would not skip down the road with her children in case the neighbours saw her and thought she was silly. She won't go swimming because she is too embarrassed about her figure. She won't go to exercise classes because she thinks the other women there will be fitter and more attractive than her and she hates how she looks in a leotard. She would not even consider skipping or riding a bike or playing a board game, because that is kids' stuff and she has far more important things to do, like cleaning the house, doing the laundry, getting ready for work and so on. When her children are being silly and childlike and noisy she will say without thinking: *Stop being childish, act your age*. She is a loving mother, but is unaware of the need sometimes to join in the silliness and be childlike too. I heard myself saying to my daughter *Stop being a baby* when she was only 11 months old. I remember thinking *Why am I saying that? She is a baby and she is allowed to be a baby*. Luckily I have learnt so much and now have such a different awareness that I don't do that sort of thing any more.

Sara, on reading the report about trampolines reducing

wrinkles and bags under the eyes, will be buying one straight away. She wouldn't stop to think *I haven't got anywhere to put it, it will spoil my bedroom and I will feel embarrassed having to explain to my husband what it is for.* She might even use her trampoline in her garden, and far from caring what the neighbours thought, she would be telling everyone about this new and wonderful way of looking and feeling younger and maybe even inviting them to try it out. Sara would do rebounding with her children, and act more like them instead of wanting them to act like her. When she decides to join in a class, she will find one for women who are out of shape and go to that first until she is in better shape, rather than avoiding classes. One of my patients became so committed to exercising that she ran when it was dark, either at dusk or early in the morning, because she was severely overweight and did not want to be seen but was determined to exercise, so she found a way.

To stay young, do new things – monotony ages anyone, and variety is the spice of life. People who are young always look forward to something, and they also look forward to new things. They must have heard the expression: *When hope dies old age runs to meet you.*

Mental Exercise

Using this chapter, make a list in your workbook of all the things you can do that will make you feel younger and that will make your body become younger – things that appeal to you, that you will be able to do and will want to do. Now decide when you are going to engage in these activities and set aside the time. Write the time in your workbook and commit to keeping to it. Choose things that physically and mentally keep you young, e.g. rebounding, playing board games, skipping, laughing, brain-teasers.

Next, find some music that you love. Make a tape of all your favourite songs and play it when you are doing the physical exercises. Make a copy of it to keep in your car, so you can play it any time and it becomes like an anchor for lifting your spirits and reminding you that you are as young as you choose to feel at any given moment.

Physical Exercise

Take something physical from this chapter and engage in it now for five or ten minutes. Notice how good it feels. Don't worry if you feel slightly silly – that feeling will soon go, and the benefits to your cells will soon compensate you.

Put on some music from the past and allow yourself to dance to it.

Play some music with a message about youth and sing out loud to it.

Ride a bike or go on a pogo stick.

Bounce on a trampoline.

Skip with a skipping rope or skip down the street.

Play hopscotch.

Fly a kite.

Play some board or card games from your childhood.

Find something funny – an article, cartoon or film – and look at the section that makes you laugh every day. When you have exhausted this, find another.

If you have friends who are funny, hang around with them more. Giggle and laugh and do childlike things on a very frequent basis.

Rent a children's film like *Mary Poppins* or *Fantasia*. Enjoy watching it – be like a child again.

Splash in the rain, have a snowball fight, be spontaneous.

Recreate all the wonderful feelings you had when you first fell in love.

Eat an ice lolly, or bake some children's cakes and biscuits and decorate them as a child would.

Paint and draw and crayon. Have fun. Make clay models.
Ride a donkey along the seafront, go to the zoo, watch Punch and Judy.
Observe how children are and become more like them.

Exercises To Test Your Biological Age

Since we are now in a new section of the programme, the understanding section, it is appropriate at this stage that you begin to understand how your body is ageing biologically. So we are going to end Day Four by having you do some tests that will establish your biological age. As you do these tests it is important to remember that your organs age on their own timetable. You could have younger eyes and older lungs, especially if you smoke; therefore you will need to mark yourself separately on each test and then work out an average to get your biological age. You will do this a second time with Test 7, to again score your biological age. It is quite hard to work out an accurate biological age using standard across-the-board tests; many of these tests work out an average without taking into account that your organs are all ageing on their own timetable with at least thirteen different measurements needing to be taken; also, with the flexibility test, allow for differing leg, arm and trunk lengths. However, with these tests you will get a good idea of how you are ageing biologically, and you will notice that your ageing is improving as you adhere to this programme and re-test yourself at intervals.

Should you discover your biological age is higher than your chronological age, do not despair. If you adhere to the programme in this book and re-test yourself in a few weeks, you will notice your biological age becoming younger.

Be sure to note down your score in your workbook, so you can compare it with later scores as you go through the programme and notice yourself becoming biologically younger.

1. Test For Balance

Stand barefoot on the floor, keep both feet together and close your eyes. Using your left foot if you are right-handed and your right foot if you are left-handed, lift your foot 6 inches off the floor with your knee bent. Time yourself to see how long you can hold this position without either opening your eyes or lowering your foot. Do this three more times and work out your average score.

SECONDS	BIOLOGICAL AGE
28 seconds	20–30
22 seconds	30–40
18 seconds	40–50
10 seconds	50–60
4 seconds	60–70

2. Test For Reactions

Get a friend to hold an 18-inch ruler vertically in front of you with the 1-inch mark at the top, hold the thumb and middle finger of one hand 3.5 inches apart beneath it. When your friend drops the ruler catch it as quickly as you can and note the inch mark at which you catch it. Do it two more times to get an average using your right, then your left, then both hands.

INCHES	BIOLOGICAL AGE
11 inches or more	20
9 inches	30
8 inches	40
7 inches	50
6 inches or less	60+

3. Test For Skin Elasticity

Place your hand on a flat surface with the fingers splayed out. Now pinch the skin on the back of one hand with the thumb and index finger of the other hand, hold for 5 seconds and let go, then count the number of seconds it takes for the skin to return to its previous condition free of puckering and ridging.

SECONDS	BIOLOGICAL AGE
Less than 1 second	20–30
Over 2 seconds	30–40
5 seconds or less	under 50
6–10 seconds	under 60
10–21 seconds	over 60

4. Nail Test

Place one of your finger-nails under a bright light. Looking at it close up and from all angles, notice:

NAIL CONDITION	BIOLOGICAL AGE
Clear healthy nail	20–30
Slightly ridged	30–40
Obvious ridging	40–50
Dry with obvious ridging	50–60
Discoloured and very noticeable or extreme ridging	60 plus

5. Test For Flexibility

Sit on the floor with your right leg stretched out ahead of you and the sole of your left foot placed against your inner right thigh. Now stretch your right arm as far as you can towards your toes and make a note of how far you can reach. Make sure you stretch from the waist, not the shoulders. Avoid rounding your back. This exercise can be done sitting on a chair with one leg on a second chair that is the same height or slightly lower and the other leg on the floor.

FLEXIBILITY	BIOLOGICAL AGE
Reaching past your toes with your fingers	20–30
Reaching your toes with your fingers	30–40
Reaching your ankle with your fingers	40–50
Reaching mid-calf with your fingers	60s

6. Test For Eyesight

Hold a book or newspaper at arm's length, then bring the page towards you until the print blurs. Now measure the distance between yourself and the page. According to your age and eyesight you should be able to see the words quite clearly from your arm's length to a distance of:

INCHES	BIOLOGICAL AGE
5 inches or less	20–25
6–10 inches	26–30
8–13 inches	30–40
10–15 inches	40–50
13–25 inches	50s
39 inches or less	60s

7. Biological Age

In your workbook write down your chronological age. Add and subtract to it from the table below to reach your biological age.

If you exercise regularly, subtract	4
If your exercise recovery rate is quick, subtract	1
If you sleep easily and regularly, subtract	2
If you have a healthy sex life, subtract	2
If your endurance and breathing are good, subtract	1
If you laugh a lot, subtract	2
If you are optimistic by nature, subtract	2
If your diet is healthy, subtract	2
If you are overweight by more than 10 per cent, add	2
If your diet is unhealthy, add	2
If you have poor digestion, add	2
If you smoke, add	4
If you drink every day, add	2
If you get depressed often, add	2
If you often get ill, colds, aches and pains, add	2
If you get breathless, add	1
If you sunbathe frequently, add	2

TO RECAP

Today, on Day Four, you have learnt the importance of acting as if you were young on a regular basis, of not taking yourself too seriously.

You have learnt that when you do young things your body literally grows younger.

You have learnt that something as simple as

• laughing and giggling

- singing and dancing
- listening to happy music from the past
- skipping and jumping

can cause us instantly to regress back to our youth, not just with our thoughts but also with our bodies.

You have learnt how to test your biological age.

You have learnt how to keep your mind and body young.

Thought For The Day
People don't grow old; when they stop growing they become old.

ANON

Quote
You are only as old as the person you feel.

GROUCHO MARX

DAY 5

How the Mind Works

After yesterday's day of moving about and doing physical things, we are spending today, our fifth day, working again on the power of the mind. Today, on Day Five of our programme, you are going to learn how your mind works, the rules of the mind, so that you can fully influence your mind rather than being influenced by thoughts and behaviours that you don't want.

Imagine if you went out and bought the most up-to-date computer or a wonderful video recorder or washing-machine and it came with NO instructions. How would you use it? You might find that you could not use it at all, or you might muddle through, but you would never get the best out of your machine – you could never use it to its full capacity and you would not get the excellent results that it was capable of giving you.

The same thing happens with humans. We come into this world with the most amazing computer-like brain, capable of doing so much, but there are no instructions that tell us how to get the best from ourselves, no manual that shows us how to programme ourselves for success. So we muddle through when we are capable of so much more.

We can buy an abundance of books telling us how to raise our children, but they don't tell us how to show them how to run their minds for success. You can find instructions on how to take charge of your body, weight and shape, but very little on how to run your mind. This situation is changing slowly, however, and there are some books and courses available now that will point you in the right direction. Some of them are excellent, and I look forward to the day when this information is taught in schools.

Here are a list of the rules of the mind as they apply to ageing. By reading them you will have still more understanding of yourself.

1. Every thought or idea causes a physical reaction

Throughout the first section of this book I have talked about thoughts having consequences and creating changes in the body, on thoughts creating chemical reactions in the body, so I won't repeat this information here.

Ideas that have a strong emotional content always reach the subconscious mind because it is the feeling mind. Once accepted, these ideas create the same reactions in the body again and again. To change negative reactions in the body it is important to change the ideas responsible for the reaction both consciously and subconsciously.

So if you have strong negative emotions linked to ageing, they will move into your subconscious mind and have a very real effect on you, whereas by changing so that your emotions are positive you can ensure that the effect your thoughts and emotions have on you is positive too.

2. What is expected tends to be realized

The brain and nervous system respond only to mental images, regardless of whether the image is self-induced or from the external world. The mental image formed becomes the blue-print, and the subconscious mind uses every means at its disposal to carry out the plan. Worrying is a form of programming a picture of what we don't want, but the subconscious mind acts to fulfil the picture situation.

Therefore never worry about getting old, but decide instead to defy, challenge and redefine ageing. Our physical health can be absolutely linked to our mental expectancy – if we expect to get ill, if we say *I'm bound to get a cold because I got caught in the rain or put on damp clothes*, then we usually will. Instead of expecting a decline into poor health as you get older, remove every despondent and negative attitude about ageing and expect to age fabulously. Expect to maintain health, strength and a feeling of well-being, expect to continue to look and feel great, and these expectations will be realized.

3. Imagination is more powerful than knowledge when dealing with your own mind or the mind of another

Reason is easily overruled by imagination. Violence would be unheard of if logic were able to override the emotional reaction. We can all stand on a piece of wood on the floor, but if that piece of wood became a window ledge high up, the imagination of falling off becomes more powerful than the knowledge that we can stand there if we have to. Any idea accompanied by a strong emotion such as anger, hatred, jealousy, or religious or political beliefs is more powerful than any logical information meant to disprove it.

Your imagination and your ability to see yourself as younger, to believe you can slow down ageing, is more powerful than any data that say it can't be done.

Since science now says it *can* be done, and since there is well-documented proof of examples of age reversal, we really have no reason to age prematurely.

4. Each suggestion acted upon creates less opposition to successive suggestion

Once a suggestion has been accepted by the subconscious mind it becomes easier for additional suggestions to be accepted and acted upon.

So if we assume that this book has already caused you to accept some new suggestions, you can take faith in the knowledge that this alone is making it easier for you, for your mind to accept further beneficial information.

5. An emotionally induced symptom tends to cause organic changes if persisted in long enough

It has been acknowledged by many doctors that more than 75 per cent of human ailments are functional rather than organic, meaning that the function of an organ or other body part has been disturbed by the reaction of the nervous system to negative ideas held in the subconscious mind.

We cannot separate the mind from the body, so if you dread ageing and constantly focus on getting old, on feeling and looking older, if you are searching for new wrinkles and looking for grey hairs, then in time negative organic changes must occur. If you welcome and enjoy every stage of your life and expect to stay young while living longer, then positive organic changes must occur.

6. When dealing with the subconscious mind and its functions, the greater the conscious effort, the less the subconscious response

Will-power is not the tool to use when implementing change. We've all tried to remember something, tried really hard and yet haven't remembered it, and then found that as we stop trying, the information we are looking for springs to mind.

This is because the more conscious effort we make the less the subconscious responds. Trying to go to sleep doesn't work for an insomniac. If you wake up from a dream that has occurred in the subconscious mind, then try to remember it consciously; it doesn't really work – it is easier to close your eyes and go back into a subconscious state to recall the dream.

When you are making physical changes by using exercise, it is true that the more effort you put in the more results you will get back. But when you are making mental changes, when you are changing your thoughts, beliefs and expectations, the opposite applies. You don't need to try, you just need to let your subconscious absorb these new ideas, to accept them, to have new expectations which will be met. When making mental changes, effort is not truly necessary – what is necessary is the ability to get an image of how you plan to be, hold that image in your mind, relax into the image, use language that matches the image, and keep re-running the image so you are rehearsing it to such an extent that your brain thinks: *I have been here before, I know how to do this, it's easy.*

As you take on new beliefs about ageing you will replace all the old negative ones, but you must do it fully, you must pro-gramme your subconscious mind specifically. Form good images about ageing in your subconscious mind, which is the feeling mind and can remove, alter or amend old ideas and beliefs.

7. Once an idea has been accepted by the subconscious mind it remains until it is replaced by another idea

The companion rule to this is:

8. The longer the idea remains, the more opposition there is to replacing it with a new idea

Once an idea has been accepted it tends to remain. The longer it is held the more it tends to become a fixed habit of thinking.

This is how habits of action are formed, both good and bad. First is the habit of thought and next the habit of action. We have habits of thinking as well as habits of action; however, the thought or idea always comes first. Therefore if we want to change our actions we must begin by changing our thoughts.

It has been said *We First Make Our Habits and Then Our Habits Make Us.*

We have many thought habits which are incorrect but are still fixed in the mind. Some people believe that at critical times they must have a drink to steady their nerves, or a tranquillizer to calm them down. This is not necessarily true – the tranquillizer they take could even be a placebo, but the idea is there and it is a fixed habit of thought.

There can be opposition to replacing it with a correct idea. These are fixed ideas, not fleeting thoughts, but no matter how fixed the ideas are or how long they have been held, they can absolutely be changed. As I mentioned earlier, we have different kinds of beliefs. We have:

- CONVICTIONS: They can be evaluated over time otherwise your conviction becomes your jailer.
- OPINIONS: They can easily be changed because they are often temporary, based on information, and don't have emotion invested in them.

Strong beliefs in particular have emotion tied to them and need work to change them. All beliefs can be changed if you introduce doubt; because the minute you begin to question something you no longer really believe it. Ask someone if their partner is faithful and they will have a belief or a conviction, but if you suggest to them that you know otherwise, that you have information that they are seeing someone else, you may put doubt in their mind. It very much depends on their belief system. Ask someone if they believe in God, and most people who are religious are in no doubt and won't question their beliefs.

Now look at all your beliefs about ageing, about how you expect to age – are they opinions or are they convictions?

You will find all the information in this book to allow you to introduce doubt into any belief, conviction, or opinion about ageing that is negative.

9. The mind cannot hold conflicting beliefs

The mind cannot hold conflicting thoughts. We can't be honest and dishonest at the same time or happy and sad simultaneously. If you hold conflicting beliefs it sends the mind into a spin, it blocks the mind.

Making lots of jokes about the supposed horrors of getting old, and exaggerating in jokes what we perceive as ageing, does this. We cannot plan to age well and then engage in joking about the awfulness of ageing, because the beliefs are contradictory – they confuse the mind, which has to take everything we say as the truth as literal.

Joking about ageing links pain to ageing. We are run by what we link pain and pleasure to; people who are successful in any area – relationships, health, career – have very clear definitions.

For example, if you long to be in love but fear becoming vulnerable when this happens, or one day being rejected by your lover, then you are linking pleasure and pain to the same thing and the mind can't move forwards. If you want to be hugely successful but link pain to hard work, or to not having your weekends free, then you have mixed associations which you must change.

Bulimics are an interesting example of mixed associations because they link pain and pleasure to food. They hate being full and yet love being full, they love food and they detest even the smell of it, they love the feeling of having an empty stomach and they loathe it. They usually think of food all day yet want to be indifferent to food.

Changing our associations makes life so much easier, and humans are the only creatures lucky enough to be able to choose what they associate pain or pleasure with. It has been said that this is both the major advantage and disadvantage of humans. A cat can't choose to love water any more than a polar bear could choose to love the tropics. But humans are so lucky, so privileged, they can choose what to link pain or pleasure to. I can choose to love eating meat or to link pain to it and thus become a vegetarian, but I would find it hard if I linked pleasure to meat while deciding to give it up. If I hate exercising and link pain to it but feel I have to do it and I must do it, it will always be a chore, but if I decide I want to exercise, that I will enjoy it, it becomes more of a pleasure.

Whatever changes you make as a result of reading this book, link pleasure to them. If you hate exercising but make yourself do it, you will lose some of its benefits. If you give up junk food but resent doing so, your mind will link pain to healthy eating and you may always feel deprived, instead of knowing that you have made some life-enhancing choices and feeling great and proud about them.

Don't say *I must*, *I have to*, or *I have got to* — say *I want to*, *I have chosen to*. It is such a simple change and yet it makes such a big difference.

When I was first writing this book I had some resistance to spending my weekends writing. Friends would invite me over and I would say *I can't, I have to write my book*, but when I began to say *I want to write this weekend* I felt entirely different and noticed I was enjoying the process. I hypnotize a lot of students around examination time, and I always tell them that they have chosen to study, that for this particular month they want to revise, that it is compelling, that they actually enjoy the process, that it makes them feel so good to do the work. They almost always send in friends who say *You hypnotized my friend to study and it's amazing, he/she is actually enjoying it — can you do the same for me, please?*

If you make a point of linking massive pleasure to the changes you are making, you will move towards them easily. If you link huge amounts of pain to being inactive, to smoking, to ingesting pollutants, you will move away from them more easily. Link pleasure to changing years, since you are able to choose how you feel; don't link pain, despair or fear to getting older, or you will accelerate the process. You cannot plan to look, feel and become years younger while at the same time dreading the process.

Your mind is programmed to move you towards pleasure and away from pain, and it will always do more to avoid pain than it will to seek pleasure. This is why many people won't risk talking to a stranger they are attracted to, or asking for a favour. The pain of possible rejection is more powerful than the pleasure they might gain.

Moving away from pain is a survival instinct built into our system, so that if you link pain to ageing you will always hanker after youth and always feel disadvantaged. If you link pleasure to changing, if you change your thoughts, you will change your reality and be able to become younger.

Mental Exercise

EXERCISE 1

Imagine your brain is like a telephone exchange, with wires running to different terminals, and that you are going to rewire it. Visualize a wire that is headed *pain* and links to negative pictures, words and thoughts about ageing, and another wire linking pleasure only to youth.

Now change the wiring by imagining and linking a lot of pleasure – huge, enormous amounts of pleasure – to influencing how you age. Use pictures and words to create good images of yourself looking and feeling good at every stage of your life, so that you link pleasure to getting older, wiser and happier.

Now, using negative words and images, link massive amounts of pain to holding on to the belief that only youth is good or desirable. See how ridiculous and untrue this belief is; remind yourself that the highest suicide group in the world are young people, teenagers.

Imagine yourself as a telephonist, moving wires to more

appropriate terminals, attaching the right images and words to ageing, linking pleasure to your ability to age in a way that suits you and inspires others. You can even draw this as a plan or diagram or write it out in your journal under the headings 'pain' and 'pleasure'.

How to Make Affirmations Work for You

An affirmation is simply a short statement you repeat to yourself over and over for a few minutes daily; something like:

> *I am becoming younger all the time*, or
> *I am taking the correct action that makes me look, feel and become younger*, or
> *I am a walking, talking expression and example of youthfulness.*

You repeat it over and over out loud to yourself to allow your subconscious mind to accept it, but this will not always happen instantly because we often pick an affirmation that conflicts with some beliefs we may have. One of the reasons we are discussing affirmations at this point is because by now you will have changed some beliefs and will be open to the idea of changing more.

Many people give up with affirmations because their mind seems to have so many objections to them. They don't really believe what they are saying, or understand that there is a system for having the mind accept and believe affirmations, so they find the process frustrating and abandon it. I have found that the best way to overcome this is to write out each affirmation as a statement and then just notice any objections that come to mind.

Next, write out each objection your mind may come up with. Keep on writing out the affirmation and writing out any objections or thoughts that come to mind directly underneath the affirmations in your workbook. It is important not to spend time attempting to analyse the objections, just write them out and keep going. It is worth writing out each affirmation and the consequent objection or response between ten and fifteen times.

As you review the response and the objections written out in your workbook, you will notice quite a distinct pattern emerging because the more you keep writing out the affirmation the fewer objections your mind will come up with.

Eventually your mind will exhaust the objections and it will simply say:

OK, I AGREE, I ACCEPT IT, YOU ARE BECOMING YOUNGER ALL THE TIME.

Here is an example. You decide to say out loud each day as your affirmation:

I AM BECOMING AND REMAINING YOUNGER.

Your mind may immediately come up with some objections, especially if you have been conditioned by the beliefs of others. It may go something like this:

You cannot become younger.
It is not possible to become younger.
How can anyone stay younger?
I have never heard of anyone remaining younger.
Everyone will laugh at me if I do this.
This is all rubbish.
I don't believe in this.
Actually I do believe in this.
There are examples of people growing younger.
If other people can do it, so can I.
OK, it's true, I can and will become younger.

As you continue to write out each affirmation and to say it out loud, your objections will become weaker and weaker. You will pay them less and less attention, and your belief in your affirmation will become stronger. Eventually your mind will run out of objections and will then fully accept the affirmation. Get into the habit of repeating your affirmations daily. Make sure you say them out loud. It doesn't matter if you feel silly – most people do initially – just become aware of how you feel and the thoughts and feelings coming up as you say each affirmation.

It also helps to repeat your affirmations at night just before you go to sleep, and again in the morning just after waking, when your subconscious is at its most receptive. It is a very good idea to write out your affirmations and to pin them up on a mirror, or on the fridge door; put them in your Filofax or on your desk and anywhere else that suits you and makes you remind yourself of them regularly and frequently. By doing this you will be able to make your life and yourself and your ability to look and feel and become younger an ongoing, breathing affirmation. You will develop more and more potential through the use of your affirmations, because the words and images you repeat over and over to yourself become the blueprint for who you become.

Positive affirmations go into the subconscious and eventually replace negative thoughts. The subconscious responds the most to clear authoritative commands; the more clear, precise and straightforward they are, the more rapidly the mind accepts them and goes to work on them. Affirmations can also build self-esteem, make you more optimistic, and diminish negative self-talk.

EXERCISE 2

Write out your affirmations in your workbook, using the instructions above, and write out every objection you come up with until you have exhausted them. Do this at least fifteen times, then look at all your reactions and see what you can learn from them.

More examples of affirmations are:

> *My body is ageless.*
> *I am a wonderful example of ageless ageing.*
> *I am ageless.*

I have abundant energy.
I exercise regularly and have excellent recovery time.
I am proving to all who know me that life can grow younger.

Well done for finishing Day Five — you are now half-way through your programme and have done 50 per cent of the work that will allow you to become younger.

TO RECAP

Today, on Day Five, you have learnt the rules of the mind and how they apply to ageing.
 You have learnt that:

- Every thought or idea causes a physical reaction in the body.
- What is expected with regard to ageing tends to be realized.
- Imagination is more powerful than knowledge.
- Each suggestion about ageing acted upon creates less opposition to the next suggestion.
- The greater the conscious effort the less the subconscious responds.
- The mind cannot hold conflicting beliefs.
- How to make affirmations work for you.
- How to become a walking, talking expression of your affirmations.

Thought For The Day
If you do what you have always done you get what you have always got.

Quote
Age only matters if you are wine.

ANON

How to Programme Your Mind to Age Well

How to Programme the Subconscious Mind

Today, on Day Six, we are going to learn how to programme our minds easily and effectively to look, feel and become years younger. The Stanford Brain Institute says we use only 2 per cent of our brain, so we have vast potential to tap into.

We all have an imagination, or we would never worry or respond to images in the cinema. I frequently meet clients who say *I can't imagine things, I'm no good at visualization*.

I sometimes say *That's wonderful – you must never have a day's worry in your life*.

When they reply *Oh, but I do*, I gently reply *How can you worry if you can't imagine or visualize?*

How do you find your car when you return to the car park if you don't have the ability to visualize where you parked it hours earlier?

Visualization takes practice. It will get easier, because what the mind sees it believes without question. What you can hold in your mind you can accomplish, and as you visualize you will stimulate your mind and body into action.

Everyone has an imagination, and your imagination has no limits. If you feel you can't *see* you or your cells becoming younger, remember the power of thought – thinking of it will make it happen. Your mind is actually seeing it in great detail; you are just not aware of it.

You can learn to see yourself as young and you can see yourself staying young and even becoming younger. Everything that happens is linked to how we see ourselves. You can and will become younger to the degree that you are able to see yourself as youthful. If you practise skills of visualization and combine them with programming the subconscious mind, you will get very definite results.

We have amazing potential to influence our cells, to tell them how to behave and have them act accordingly. I always describe cells as rather like schoolchildren in that they know exactly what to do and how to do it, but if they have started to break down or malfunction they need to be commanded, instructed and told or shown what to do, using the power of thought, visualization and imagination.

You won't believe it when you see it. You will see it when you believe it. What we see and believe is what we ultimately become.

The scripts in Day Eight go into this in great detail; they use the power of thought and imagination to direct cells to act as younger cells do. Your mind already has a memory of how cells performed when they were younger, and you can manifest this just by thinking of it. This means that as you think about cells performing in a particular way, you can activate their ability to do it. If you think about swallowing, it will make you want to swallow. If you think about scratching your nose, you will find your nose starting to itch because your thoughts turn into effects in the body.

After thinking this, and practising this for a few days, you will find that the words and descriptions become embedded in your mind and you can relate and refer to them easily and automatically. This will have an effect on your skin, its collagen, its elastin, your organs and on your sense of well-being. Even as you sleep your subconscious mind is affecting your hormones, increasing blood flow affecting your skin and skin cells and your muscles, which have a memory all of their own.

Your subconscious mind is much stronger than your conscious mind. It is said that only 10 per cent of our mind is conscious, the other 90 per cent is all subconscious. Willpower accounts for only 4 per cent of our minds. The conscious mind is the mind of choice while the subconscious is the mind of preference, so we always choose what we prefer.

In areas of conflict the subconscious mind will always win, because it can make the conscious do whatever it likes. This is very relevant in areas such as overeating, where the conscious desire may be to be slim, but the subconscious has some deeper preference for the excess weight – often as a form of insulation or barrier.

Some hypochondriacs have a strong conscious desire to be well but the subconscious desire to be ill, because it allows them to receive attention, love, touch, time, nurturing, concern, etc., is at least 90 per cent stronger. The subconscious mind also works 30,000 times faster than the conscious, so if you are set on making changes but think you only have to make them consciously, you will find it a harder, longer and less successful process than if you make those changes subconsciously.

If you want to change any behaviour be sure to make changes consciously and subconsciously. Your subconscious mind only has one job to do, and that is to move you towards pleasure and away from pain, so what you link pain and pleasure to can and will rule you, unless you are able to change the associations with pleasure and pain as you go through life as you learnt on day five.

If you link pleasure to smoking and believe that it is relaxing or calming or helps you concentrate, and link pain to times when you can't smoke, then later on, when you reach a time in your life when you decide to stop smoking, it can be difficult, unless you first change those associations on a subconscious level.

Your mind will always do what it *thinks* you want it to, but unless you are clear when programming your mind, it will do things with the right intention but often getting the wrong result. It is rather like having someone come in to clean your house, moving all your things and putting them back in the wrong place. Their intention is to help you, but unless you are able to state clearly what you want, to say *Don't move the papers on my desk, don't throw out that pile of magazines but please do this and this*, you won't get the result you intended, and would have got if you had been more clear and more detailed in your instructions.

You must be absolutely specific in what you tell your mind, since your mind has no capacity to reason and will lock on to ideas which are not specific or detailed enough. If this happens you won't get the results you want and could have. For instance, if someone longed for attention they might develop a nervous habit which would certainly get them lots of attention but not the kind they wanted. If you want attention, make sure you programme your subconscious by letting it know that you only want *positive* attention.

When children want attention they don't care if it's positive or negative. Some children and adults can get a variety of illnesses because they are not getting the attention they need, and sometimes the subconscious need or desire for attention can be so great that it can cause a person to go from one symptom of illness to another, completely overruling the conscious desire to be fit and well.

If you long for a rest because you are overworked and then end up in bed with flu, this is an example of the subconscious being incorrectly programmed. The same applies to dreading going to a party or a meeting and waking up on the said day with a stomach-ache or headache that prevents you from going.

I once worked with a girl who was late for everything, which caused her lots of anxiety and unhappiness. She realized while in hypnosis that this had started as a child, when she was desperate for attention and would miss the school bus so that her father would have to drive her to school. As an adult she continued the pattern of being late and getting lots of unwanted attention, as she was a teacher and would always be the last into her own classroom. When she went to a lecture or concert she would always be the last one to enter the room, so that everyone would turn to look at her or stand up to let her pass. She hated this, but it got her lots of attention.

She was able to change this behaviour by letting her subconscious know that it was outdated and inappropriate, caused her anxiety, had a negative effect on her career, and did not get her the kind of attention she wanted at all. As she told herself that she only wanted positive and beneficial attention, she ceased being late and actually started to get to places early. She was delighted with this, because it made such a difference to her life. She was calmer, she no longer missed trains or appointments, and she was able to develop a reputation for being punctual, although it took her friends and family a while to get used to the new behaviour.

In the area of looking, feeling and becoming younger it is unlikely there will be any conflict, especially since by this stage of the book you will have worked through them, but it is great to understand how the subconscious works because it is so powerful and such a wonderful asset to have. Once you learn how to programme your mind to your advantage you will see that your mind is a great ally – it will do what you ask and tell it to do if you ask it in a specific way.

Your mind is the most effective and powerful tool for implementing positive changes in your life. If you follow the steps overleaf you will become an expert at programming your subconscious mind, and you will find that:

> The more you do it,
> The better you become at it,
> The more you enjoy it, and thus
> The more you do it.

Steps to Programming the Subconscious Mind

1. Be positive

Eliminate every possible negative word and association connected with ageing. Focus only on what you wish to achieve and move towards.

2. Be absolutely clear

Keep your mind on what you want and off what you don't want. Whatever you focus on you will move towards, so thinking about how you don't want to look or feel or become simply puts negative words and images back into your mind.

Example: *I feel excited and positive about every stage of my life.*
    Not   *I am not scared about getting older.*

Example: *I am looking and feeling younger all the time.*
    Not   *I don't look old and I don't feel old.*

Example: *My energy level is great, I have abundant energy.*
    Not   *I no longer feel as tired as I used to.*

No, not, don't are all neutral words and have no effect on the subconscious mind. Thinking *I am not sleepy, I don't feel tired* causes the mind to lock on to the only descriptive words in the sentence, which are *tired, sleepy*.

If you keep saying *I don't feel ill*, your mind is locking on to the descriptive word *ill*, so replace it with: *I feel wonderfully healthy*.

Thinking *I am not getting older* focuses on the only descriptive word, which is *older*, so replace it with: *I am young, I am an expression of youthfulness*.

By turning over any negative thoughts you will find the positive, because they are the flip side of your thinking.

3. Be specific, use very descriptive words

The words we use in front of words increase or decrease the effect of those words. Rather than saying *I feel healthy*, say *I feel extremely healthy or fantastically healthy, I have abundant energy, massive amounts of energy*. Instead of saying *I like playing tennis*, change it to *I am passionate about tennis and feel invigorated after every game*.

The mind only responds to words that are symbolic, that make a picture, so use words that are very symbolic and descriptive, i.e.

> *I have smooth, satiny skin.*
> *I am flexible, supple and agile.*
> *I enjoy vigorous health.*
> *I have tremendous stamina.*
> *I look and feel marvellous.*
> *I have perfect cell regeneration.*

Don't worry if this all seems a little far-fetched and not strictly true. Your subconscious mind has no capacity to reason and will believe whatever you tell it, if you tell it often enough, so you may as well go for it and exaggerate every point.

There are 750,000 words in the English language, but many people use only 1,200 of them. There are 4,000 words for emotions and feelings, yet many people use the same twelve words over and over to describe how they are feeling, words like *not bad, pretty good, OK, all right*. Using different words will change your biochemistry, so when you are describing yourself use words like *magnificent, amazing, fabulous, excellent, phenomenal, superb, enthusiastic, outstanding, exceptional, dynamic, wonderful, marvellous*, etc.

4. Use the present tense

The subconscious mind works only in the present, so create images that are occurring now, this instant. Use a progressive form of self-hypnosis for conditions which need time to change, for example injuries, body weight, skin conditions, etc.

Example: *My skin is becoming more clear, healthy and attractive every day.*
            The ulcer is healing rapidly and progressively right now.

Never use the word *my* as a prefix to something you wish to be free of.
My migraines, my wrinkles, my fat legs, my addiction, my pain, my headaches, my cellulite.
This is making the mind accept something as belonging to you when it doesn't.
A good rule of thumb is: if you don't want to keep it, don't call it *mine*.
Your mind finds it much easier to change things and let go of things when it believes you don't want them, but if you call those same things *mine* it is very confusing to the mind.
One of the rules of the mind is: *The mind cannot hold conflicting beliefs.*
It becomes easy and habitual to say *the headache, the cellulite, the wrinkles.* So start doing it now. If you have a pain, instead of saying *My arm aches*, or *My pain is* . . . , or *My headache* . . . say *The pain is* and so on.

If your programming says: *Next year or even next month I will look and feel younger*, your mind won't make an image of it because it only works in the present. So you must say: *I look younger now.*

It is very beneficial to add the words *now* or *right now* to the end of every statement you make. For example,

> *My cells are repairing and replacing themselves perfectly right now.*
> *I am looking, feeling and becoming younger now.*
> *I am absorbing and benefiting from my vitamins right now.*

5. Be detailed

Make your words dynamic and descriptive – *I am young, vibrant and full of life.*
Make it personal – *I am, I look, I always, I can, I feel.*

6. Visualization must be vivid

See it, sense it, feel it, touch it, hear it, activate all your senses. The more vividly you visualize, the more rapidly your mind responds.
See yourself as young, **feel** yourself enjoying excellent health. **Imagine** touching your skin and it **feels** soft and satiny. **Sense** your body responding to your instructions so that every cell is in the right place at the right time, doing its work perfectly. **Hear** people commenting on how well, how young you look.

7. Visualization must be frequent

Repeat it over and over again, like playing a video in your head.

8. Use duration and intensity

Hold the picture for longer and make it bigger, brighter and clearer.
   Combining visualization with intensity of desire increases effectiveness.

Visualization takes practice.
   What the mind sees it believes without question. Your ability to visualize will have a powerful effect on you.
   As you visualize you will stimulate your mind and body into action. Remember, what you can hold in your mind with confidence and feeling you can achieve.
   Become more and more clear about what you want. The

more you visualize, the more you will believe your visualization is possible.

Very successful people visualize all the time.

We can all change our thinking and the mental pictures we make, and as we improve them we can improve everything. By changing your thinking and your focus and by making changes in the language you use, you can change your looks and your health for ever.

Your body reflects your thinking.

The body you will have in ten years' time will be a reflection of the thoughts you are having connected to ageing today.

EXERCISE 1

Using your diary or workbook, make a programme for yourself using the 'Steps to Programming the Subconscious Mind' as a guide.

Go through each step from 1 to 8 and write it out as a plan, beginning at Step 1 and working down to Step 8, by which time your thought will have become one or more paragraphs.

Begin now by taking a thought such as *I am becoming younger* and write this out as number 1.

1. *I am becoming younger.*
2. Go to Step 2 and decide how you can be absolutely crystal clear about this. Write it out.
3. Now move to Step 3 and increase your sentence into a paragraph, using very descriptive words and keeping it all in the present tense.
   Example: *I am becoming younger by . . .* or *I am becoming younger because . . .* or *I am becoming younger as I . . .*
4. Make it even more personal. This is all about you as you want to be, so add more words and thoughts. Put some powerful, positive words in front of your sentences: *I am becoming amazingly younger, I am a superb and excellent example*

of youngness, My body is —, I have the energy level of — and so on. It is great to use several thoughts and then join them up as a statement as you work through this exercise. The end result will leave you with an exciting, easy-to-memorize statement about yourself rather than several lines of short sentences.

5. Make it much more detailed by adding in *I am —, I always —, I feel —, I can —, I look —, I have —,* to your programme.

6. Use and activate your senses by adding the words *feel, sense, touch, see, hear, imagine.*

7. Keep working on it until you have it exactly as you want it, then read and repeat to yourself over and over again what you have written until it becomes embedded in your mind. This will happen quite quickly and easily.

    Your programme should not be so long that you can't recall it or so short that it does not make enough impact on your mind.

8. Now you are ready to close your eyes and begin to imagine what you have created and chosen for yourself. Again, it really doesn't matter if you don't seem to make vivid pictures. By now your mind is absolutely responding to the words and images, whether you are seeing them clearly or not. A finished example of this would be:

I am becoming younger, my body is growing younger and my mind is always young. I know and feel this to be true because I think young thoughts and because I feel so young. I feel as healthy and as young as I felt in my teens; in fact I feel happier and more content and I continue to look forward to every stage of my life.

I am becoming younger by thinking young thoughts always, I am becoming younger because I have a belief system that allows me to believe and know this is possible. I am becoming younger because I have such a strong desire and belief in my ability to become Forever Young.

I am a wonderful example of the power of the mind to slow ageing. I impress and inspire people I come into contact with because I am such an expression of youth.

My body looks and feels young. I have abundant energy, I love the challenge of new things. I feel young because I believe I am young, I constantly hear people telling me how young and vibrant I am. My skin feels young and healthy and I know my cells are forever young and healthy.

When we hold a thought, plan, goal or idea continuously in our mind, our subconscious has to bring it to a reality. Many of my clients tell me they don't believe this, because they have had a plan in their minds that has never come to fruition. This is always because they have not done the groundwork, they have not cleared their mind of conflicting thoughts and beliefs beforehand. Although they may have had a plan in their minds, they have not programmed their minds in a specific way that will allow the plan to be realized.

If you follow the eight steps designed to allow you to programme your mind for success, you can only succeed. You can continue to hold your programme in your mind by writing and rewriting it, reviewing it, talking about it and visualizing it.

Some people are very visual and respond to how things look, while others respond better to how things sound or feel. This is known as being visual, auditory or kinaesthetic. Whichever you are predominantly, this programme has been designed and will work for you.

People who respond to how things look are known as visual.

People who respond to how things sound are known as auditory.

People who respond to how things feel are known as kinaesthetic.

It is possible to be a combination of all three, or to be predominantly one with aspects of the other.

If you know that you are mostly visual, then focus more in your programme on how you look. If you are more kinaesthetic, focus more on how you feel. If you are predominantly auditory you can focus on hearing how well you look.

In the same way that you get into the habit of repeating your affirmation before you fall asleep, you can also read your programme to yourself. You may find it helps you further to record your programme on to a tape and to play it back to yourself, so that you can absorb the words rather than trying to remember them. This is not essential, however, because the more you look at this programme the more your mind will retain it.

You will find you can remember the programme by focusing on it and reading it until it quickly becomes embedded in your mind. Write out the programme and pin it to your desk, your fridge or your mirror, keep a copy in your Filofax, and if you make a collage or poster add your programme to it.

If you decide to record your programme it is quite a simple process. Many personal stereos have a recording facility, as do most stereos. You may need to buy a small microphone. A small tape recorder with a recording facility will cost about £20.

Tomorrow, Day Seven, you are going to learn to put yourself into a different state of mind – a kind of self-hypnosis which is safe and easy and will allow you to programme your mind even more successfully.

Congratulations on all the work you have done today!

TO RECAP

Today, on Day Six, you have learnt:

- How to programme your subconscious mind for success.
- How to visualize perfectly even if you are not a very visual person.
- How to make a personal programme for you that you can believe in and that will excite your imagination. As you focus on this programme you will move towards its realization.

Thought For The Day
As a man thinketh in his heart so is he.

THE BIBLE

Quote
Age cannot wither her nor custom stale her infinite variety.

SHAKESPEARE

DAY 7

How to Use Self-Hypnosis

Today, on Day Seven, you are going to learn about self-hypnosis and come to understand that, far from hypnosis being something to fear, it is a wonderful and powerful aid and tool that can and will help you immensely once you know how to use it.

Many people are scared of the very idea of hypnosis. They see it as a state where they have no control or are out of control or, even worse, are controlled by someone else. The most frequently voiced fear seems to be: *What if I never come out of hypnosis?* I can assure you that hypnosis has been used since 2600 BC and this has never happened − there is not one documented case of a person remaining in hypnosis. You could not actually remain in hypnosis indefinitely. It is not possible to remain in any state of hypnosis, including self-hypnosis, indefinitely. Hypnosis is so natural that we drift in and out of it all the time, so if you took yourself into this natural state, or allowed someone else to, and they did not bring you out of it, you would simply come out of it yourself after a few moments. Or you would eventually fall into a normal state of sleep which would very soon cause you to come out of the hypnotized state.

Fears about self-hypnosis are based on myths and misconceptions. It is in fact very safe, very enjoyable, very easy and very natural – almost anyone can practice self-hypnosis. You cannot be made to do anything you don't want to do when being hypnotized, and certainly not when you are hypnotizing yourself to accept new and exciting changes in your concept of ageing. You cannot make yourself do anything you do not want to do, and neither can anyone else. No awful images or memories are going to invade your thoughts. You may have heard stories of this happening within therapeutic hypnosis, but these stories are always second-hand and highly exaggerated. Therapeutic or clinical hypnosis is very different from self-hypnosis, and in the right context of a therapeutic session painful memories or images can be recalled in order to be dealt with. However, this will not happen with you – you are merely going to use self-hypnosis to access your subconscious mind and accept ideas that you want to accept about becoming younger. You will not drift off into other areas or thoughts, and you cannot become damaged in any way at all by enjoying this pleasant, natural state of mind.

Hypnosis is not and cannot become addictive, although many people find it so effective that they practise it frequently and enjoy the benefits in the same way that someone who discovers the benefits of exercise then chooses to participate in it frequently. Many of my clients have become big fans of hypnosis because it has done so much for them. They enthuse about hypnosis and tell everyone how wonderful it is, how life-changing it has been for them, but they are not addicted to hypnosis nor have they been brainwashed by it. It is no different from someone becoming enthusiastic about the latest dance class, or restaurant, or book, and wanting to tell everyone about it.

I have been a hypnotherapist for over twelve years. I have seen thousands of clients, taught hundreds of students and hypnotized people on television. I have given live demonstrations of hypnosis to audiences of students and doctors, yet I have never made anyone do things they don't want to do. If it really was that easy to make people do what we want, all hypnotherapists would surely be millionaires with a 100 per cent success rate – we could make our clients' ailments disappear, while charging vast prices and having our clients believe they wanted to pay them.

I am aware that some hypnotists do claim these powers, and all I can tell you is to avoid them. They may like to believe they have some superior and mystical power, but it is not true. Hypnosis is not a power, it is a skill that most people can learn, which is why even adult education programmes offer training in it. Some people turn out to be better hypnotists than others, in the same way some people turn out to be better cooks or designers than others because they have a natural skill or flair for it. While almost anyone can learn self-hypnosis, other skills are needed to become a professional hypnotherapist. They include integrity, honesty, quick thinking and perception, compassion and sensory acuity.

If you feel you would like to consult a hypnotherapist, make sure you choose one who is fully trained. The College of Hypnotherapy and Hypnohealing has a register of trained therapists across Britain, and can be contacted on 01704 576285.

Hypnosis is a natural state of mind. It is absolutely safe, and far from being unaware and out of control while in hypnosis, you will actually enjoy a heightened state of awareness. The feeling it is most similar to is when you wake up in the morning but can still enjoy a few moments with your eyes closed in a semi-dreamy state – you are fully conscious, yet relaxed and at peace.

Again, you cannot be made to do anything you don't want to while in hypnosis. Since what you are going to experience is self-hypnosis, you will be taking yourself into the experience and bringing yourself out of it – you will be in full charge all the time. You will never be *under* anything – most hypnotherapists don't even use the words *under hypnosis* or *under the influence*, because it simply is not possible to be *under hypnosis*.

In the earlier chapters of this book I have made a point of not referring to hypnosis very much. This is not a book about hypnosis or hypnotherapy – it is a book about how to slow down ageing, and if you wish you can slow down ageing without ever directly using hypnosis. If you felt very anti hypnosis you could even choose to leave out the hypnosis section of this book or work around it and still get very good results. However, hypnosis is such a natural state that you already experience it several times a day without realizing it. So you are not going to be participating in anything mysterious or even new. We experience hypnosis when we drive our car on a familiar route yet are not consciously doing the driving and can get home without even an awareness of how we did it. We are enjoying a state of hypnosis when our conscious mind is absorbed by the television or a good book.

Hypnosis is a very powerful tool for implementing change, and by learning to enjoy this state and to use it to benefit yourself, to allow yourself to programme your mind and particularly your cells to become younger, which we will be doing on Day Eight and Day Nine, you will have a very powerful tool to use in defying ageing at any age.

Hypnosis has numerous benefits, one of which is that we have a critical factor in the mind that screens all our thoughts. While we are in hypnosis this critical factor shuts down and we are more receptive to ideas we previously may have rejected; however, we will only accept ideas that we want to accept. Hypnosis cannot make you accept things that have no appeal to you.

By using self-hypnosis you can allow positive suggestions about remaining young to go straight into the subconscious mind, past the conscious mind, which could reject them. However, since this book has been read consciously and has offered your conscious mind new information that is all factual, true and sometimes scientifically based, you have allowed your conscious mind to accept them as well, which gives you even more ability to remain forever young. So in effect you have reprogrammed yourself on a subconscious and a conscious level, which will make you a strong advocate, and in time a living example, of ageless ageing.

Self-hypnosis is the swiftest and shortest route into the subconscious mind, and can implement permanent changes faster than any other form of therapy. It can succeed when all other forms of therapy and healing have failed.

Six Steps to Self-Hypnosis

1 Sit or lie with your feet apart and your hands separated. Ensure that you will not be disturbed – take the phone off the hook. (Later, when you are used to self-hypnosis, you will be able to practise it in busy (even noisy) places like an airport, on a train or bus, in the park, and so on, without anyone being aware and without you being bothered by background noise.)

2 Roll your eyes back and up as if you are trying to look at your eyebrows. It is important to feel your eyes straining just a little, as looking up will give you a burst of alpha brain waves.

Now fix your eyes on a real or imagined spot on the ceiling and keep your eyes on that spot. I find it helps a lot to put a little marker made of Blu-tack or something similar on the ceiling above where you are lying or sitting, so you can focus on it.

3 Take three deep exaggerated breaths. **(i)** Inhale, hold for about 10 seconds, then exhale slowly. **(ii)** Inhale, hold for a little longer, then exhale slowly. **(iii)** Inhale, hold for as long as you can or for about 20 seconds, then exhale slowly and at the same time close your eyes without hesitating.

4 Keep your eyes closed from now on. You can open them at any time, but we focus much better internally with our eyes closed.

Take another deep breath in, and as you exhale send a wave of relaxation from your head to your toes and imagine it fully relaxing you.

Now allow a drifting, floating feeling to develop in your body.

Don't try to make it happen, just think of it happening. Imagine it and just let it happen.

Imagine a wave of relaxation washing over your body, like water in the shower going from your head to your toes and relaxing you completely.

5 Picture ten steps going down.

It helps to get the same looking-down feeling that you get as you look over a balcony or down a flight of stairs or out of an upper window.

Counting backwards from 10 to 1, hold on to that looking-down sensation and begin mentally to move down the steps, drifting deeper into relaxation with each one.

If you believe that you can't mentally see your body taking each step, just imagine your feet.

Don't worry that you cannot visualize – just thinking about the steps will cause your mind to see them even if you are unaware of it.

If you have ever worried about anything at all, then you already possess perfect visualization skills.

Use all your senses: Feel your feet touching the steps.

Hear your feet making contact with each step.

See your feet moving down step by step.

6 Now you are ready to give yourself the appropriate suggestions either to repeat to yourself the programme you devised yesterday, or to think about it fully, or to have it on a tape ready to listen to. If you decide to record your programme on to a tape, leave the first 5–10 minutes blank to give yourself the time to relax before you begin hearing your programme.

You can also time how long it takes you to complete the above six steps and leave that amount of time blank. You can also record the instructions for going into self-hypnosis on the tape as well, following them with a recording of your programme.

When you make a recording on to a tape it is easier to accept it as it is played back to you if you speak in the second person. We often do this anyway as we talk to ourselves or give ourselves instructions, saying things like: *Come on, you can do it*, or *What are you doing?* or *You know better than that*.

When you write and read back a script to yourself, you can say **I** – *I can, I am, I look, I always*.

When you record it to be played back to yourself, use the second person, **YOU** – *you are, you can, you look, you always*.

After repeating your suggestions and dwelling on the positive images for long enough (5–15 minutes), you are ready to return to full awareness.

Mentally count yourself up from 1 to 5, telling yourself that on the count of 5 you will open your eyes feeling fully aware, refreshed and relaxed. Then open your eyes and proceed with your day.

You can alter these suggestions if you practise self-hypnosis at night prior to sleeping, by telling yourself that as your programme finishes you will drift into an easy, perfect sleep.

Practise self-hypnosis frequently. Repeat it over and over, like playing a videotape in your mind. Make your images big and bright and clear, and hold them in your mind for longer and longer.

Exercises

EXERCISE 1

Your exercise for Day Seven is to practise going in and out of self-hypnosis until you feel comfortable and, as you reach that stage, to focus on your programme from Day Six. You are putting yourself into a heightened state of awareness, where your mind is receptive to the programming you created, to the words and images you came up with that have a definite and specific appeal to you, and you are responding to that programming by becoming younger both physically and mentally.

Goals and Goal-Setting for Ageing Well

Now that you are becoming so good at making changes in yourself, you are also ready to understand the power of goals and to become a successful goal–setter in the area of looking and feeling ten years younger. Tests over many years, including those done at Harvard, Yale and Cornell Universities and the famous Maslow tests, show that people who set goals are always the happiest and have a very high tendency to achieve their goals.

When you bought this book you had a goal which was to look and feel ten years younger in ten days, and at this stage in the book you are already well on your way to achieving that. Start to think now of the goals you would like to achieve for yourself in the area of ageing.

How do you want to look ten years from now?

How do you want to feel?

What do you want to be doing with your life in the future?

How do you plan to spend all these extra years, since you are intending to live longer and remain active? Make sure you have a goal that draws you forward into the future.

A study at Yale University found that less than 3 per cent of people have goals, and less than 1 per cent write down their goals or make any real and detailed plans as to how they will accomplish them. This study looked at students who graduated in 1953 and noted how many of them had goals, wrote them down, and made plans to accomplish them. Twenty years later, the study discovered that the 3 per cent who had goals and had written them out as a plan were worth more financially than the whole of the remaining 97 per cent.

As you write down your goals and how you plan to attain them, you will already be taking action towards them just by this process of writing, because our minds work in such a way that whatever we focus on we move towards. The subconscious mind is a natural goal-seeking device programmed to move us towards whatever it is we are focusing on. By focusing on your goals, by writing them out, you cannot help but activate the mechanism within yourself that moves you towards them.

Goals trigger the success mechanism within us. Simply having a goal of living longer and making plans to achieve it can make it happen. If you have a goal of becoming and remaining younger and put it into action and make plans to achieve it, you will be successful.

Medical tests have shown that people who have a goal of living can defy dying. Many dying patients have literally put off or postponed death until an important event such as a birthday or significant date has passed. They have a goal of living until then. In China they have an annual day when elders are cele-brated – it is a big event that older people look forward to the way children look forward to Christmas. More deaths occur with older people directly after this date than at any other time of year, because of the goal of living until this day.

As you think about your goal of living a long, healthy, happy life, you are already beginning to excite your imagination. As you write out your goal, your conscious mind immediately accepts the goal while your subconscious mind goes to work to turn the goal into a reality.

Our mind is a goal-seeking mechanism, whereas without goals we drift and flounder. Goals give us purpose and direction and energy, which is why all successful people actively set goals for themselves. Goal-setting is a very important and extremely easy-to-learn skill which can have such wonderful results that I believe it can only be a matter of time before it is taught in schools as an essential tool. Many of us have no idea how important goal-setting is and miss out on its benefits. A lot of people don't or won't set goals in case they fail, yet the only way you can truly fail is by not trying; anything you do is a learning experience even if it doesn't work out, but failing to try doesn't teach you anything.

As I mentioned earlier, ageing is feared, even dreaded, because the general consensus is that we are worse off as we age. However, this does not have to be the case at all. If you have goals that allow you to plan to age well, to stay young and vibrant throughout your life, you will be able to influence how you age instead of dreading ageing. You will be able to influence and control the direction of the changes that go on as you age, and instead of fearing them and seeing them as unavoidable, you will be able to control and postpone many of them.

You will also belong to an élite group, since fewer than 3 per cent of the population have any goals of becoming younger or even know that such a thing is possible. However, this situation is changing rapidly. One of my aims in writing this book is to cause that low percentage to rise. As society begins to be aware of more and more people ageing fabulously and realizes that this isn't down to luck or a fluke, or even to good genes, but because they are taking the right action and making the right choices to become younger, more people will follow suit. (As a point of interest, having good genes will usually add only about three years to your life. If both your parents live long lives that won't add more than a few years to your own lifespan, but making lifestyle changes and changing habits of thought and beliefs can add up to fifty years to your life.)

As you set your goals, remember that *What the mind can conceive and believe the mind can achieve.* The vision or the goals that you will have are important, as are your plans to reach these goals, but they don't have to match completely. You can have a goal of becoming younger, and you can plan to make the changes in this book that will allow that to happen, but the exciting thing about goals is that as you start to set them you don't always even need to know exactly how you will achieve them – your mind will move you towards them anyway.

So you can have goals of becoming younger, living longer, staying fit and active, and as you programme each goal into your mind to focus on it, your mind will already be moving you towards it even as you make the lifestyle and mental changes that will make it a reality.

One of my goals is to help change ageism by making a difference in the concept of ageing.

EXERCISE 2

1. First set your goal.
   An example could be: *I am going to live every day of my life feeling and looking ten years younger.*
2. Get a clear image of it, because vision is vital to goal-achieving.
   But have a grand vision, a great vision – you don't need to think small or safe with goals, so have great goals for ageing in the most amazing way. See yourself as a phenomenon in the area of delaying ageing. Give yourself empowering, inspiring goals that excite your imagination and give you drive and determination and a sense of certainty that you can and will look and feel younger.
3. Now commit it to paper.
   Write out your goal as a detail, so your subconscious mind has a clear image of what you want and can go to work to make it happen. Also write out all the things you are going to do to achieve your goal, from refusing to listen to people who tell you that you cannot slow ageing, to refusing to criticize yourself or use ageing language, to eating more healthy food, drinking more water and taking exercise regularly. Plan what you will do to become young, for example adopting the physiology of the young.
4. Get into the habit of looking at your goal every day. You may want to rewrite it, and I recommend that you do so frequently – your goals may change and you may want to update them. Place your written goal somewhere where you

always see it, and remember as you repeat this goal to yourself that your inner resources are already beginning to make it happen.

5. Write out the reasons you have for wanting to achieve this goal. The more reasons you come up with, the more you will excite your imagination and the more you can believe it is attainable. Even if you don't fully believe it your subconscious mind will, so don't get too caught up in this.

6. See your goals, believe in them, and have your mind concentrate on them. Play them back to yourself like a video, as if they were already in existence. Use free time, for example when you are in a queue or in stationary traffic, to replay your goal scenario, and *always* do this just before you go to sleep.

7. Find a picture of someone who is a great role model for you – an example of ageless ageing – and stick it next to your written goal so that you look at this image daily along with your goal statement. Or find a picture of yourself at your most active, doing some form of activity or sport, or looking radiant.

TO RECAP

Today, on Day Seven, you have learnt how to go into a state of mind that gives you full access to your subconscious and how to become even more effective at changing yourself for the better.

You have learnt the six steps that will take you into hypnosis, which you can use again and again in so many areas of your life.

You have learnt the motivating force of goals on a deep, subconscious level, and that your mind is a natural goal-seeking device or mechanism – it must take you to what you focus on while you must in turn focus on it in a precise, specific and detailed way.

You have learnt how to set goals in that precise, specific and detailed way that brings the desired results.

You have also learnt the difference between affirmations, goals and programmes.

Affirmations are short, precise and to the point. They are often just a sentence or a phrase or a few phrases designed to be repeated out loud so that they impact on the subconscious mind.

Goals are something you focus on and move towards by writing them out, then rewriting them as a plan in order to accomplish them, holding the goal in your conscious mind and making plans to achieve it, while finding that your subconscious mind will also accept the goal or goals and move you towards them.

A programme is longer and more detailed than an affirmation but it can still be memorized – it is something you design for yourself. You design a programme that is appropriate and specifically tailored to you, to your desire and to your goals.

A programme designed from the section 'Steps to Programming the Subconscious Mind' will excite and stimulate your imagination. A programme needs to be written out and read daily or recorded on to a tape and played back to you.

Tomorrow, Day Eight, we are going to discuss scripts. Scripts are different again, because they are written for you in the second person. They are much more detailed, and contain technical or biological language. The scripts in this book have all been written with particular elements of ageing in mind, and you will learn more about them tomorrow.

You have also learnt the benefits of self-hypnosis and how easy it is to access and influence the subconscious mind, which is the ruling, controlling mind, while in the state of self-hypnosis; you have learnt how it is even more beneficial to listen and absorb both the programme and the scripts while relaxing and enjoying this state of self-hypnosis.

Thought For The Day
If you aren't taking action to get younger you are getting older.

Quote
The journey of a thousand miles begins with the first step.

MAO TSE-TUNG

Youth is far too good to waste on children.

GEORGE BERNARD SHAW

Scripts for Becoming Younger

Today, on Day Eight of *Forever Young*, we are going to go over some varied scripts, each one dealing with a particular aspect of ageing. By now you will be getting used to your own personal programme, which you created on Day Six and listened to on Day Seven.

The difference between your programme and these scripts is that your programme is something created just for you. It should be short, just a few paragraphs, and easy to memorize so that you can think about it and repeat it to yourself regularly at any time. The scripts are longer and more detailed and have been designed for you; they contain more biological information and more biological terms and they are spoken in the second person purposefully.

You may think you have so many things to do but you will soon get used to them and find that you can say your affirmations out loud anytime – especially when looking in the mirror. You can look at your goal once a week, you can pin your programme on to your poster or on to the wall and refer to it, and you can listen to your scripts before sleeping. You will only need to spend twenty minutes a day doing this and if it is important you will be able to make time for it.

After you have chosen a script that is relevant to you, begin to read it to yourself each night before sleeping so that your mind will lock on to the words. It is fine to read it to yourself in the second person so that you are saying *you* rather than *I*. Since you will be communicating with your cells and giving your body commands you need to say *you*, for example *You are working more effectively, You are making more collagen, You are becoming stronger.* If it feels unfamiliar that's OK – you will soon get used to it. The most important thing to know is that you are using a highly successful technique of communicating with your body that gets results.

I also recommend that you record the script on to a tape and play it back to yourself each day for at least twenty-one days, and thereafter once or twice a month, to condition your mind to these new beliefs and to imprint them into your memory. On average it takes the mind twenty-one days to imprint and accept new habits and beliefs and erase old ones. Again you must record it in the second person, saying *you* rather than *I*. The scripts are written out for you exactly as they need to be read or recorded so you will find this easy.

I recommend listening to these scripts while in a state of self-hypnosis, because your subconscious mind will be fully accessed and therefore receptive to the script and to the commands and mental instructions contained within it. Your critical factor, which shuts down in hypnosis, won't come up with objections or doubts, so it will accept the suggestions more easily. However, if you are averse to the idea of hypnosis you could still close your eyes and listen to the tape because we focus differently when our eyes are shut. On the other hand, you could listen to it in a state of full awareness with your eyes wide open – it will still work, but perhaps not as rapidly.

If you decide to record the scripts and listen to them while in self-hypnosis, first record the six steps from Day Seven on to your tape to take you into self-hypnosis and then follow this by recording the suggestions from your particular script on to the same tape. You can also record the ending, counting from 1 to 5 and instructing yourself to open your eyes feeling fully aware.

When listening to these scripts it is important to know that you don't need to be a dermatologist or biochemist with a perfect knowledge of the workings of your body to get results. I do have clients who say to me, *When I listen to your tape I don't understand some of the terms or phrases. Does that mean I won't get such good results?* I can only reiterate that your body understands the terms completely and perfectly and will do the work for you – all you need to do is believe it will work, expect it to work, and see the results.

Most people when asked to place their hands on their stomach will put their hands over their intestines, because the stomach is actually under the ribs. This inability to correctly place body parts does not stop them working. You don't need a full knowledge of how your body works in order to have it work even better, in fact a knowledge of the mind–body connection in making changes will be more beneficial to you than a biological map of the body.

If your doctor were to say to you, *You have an inflamed pituitary gland*, or *a problem with your cranium*, you might be in the dark in terms of locating those body parts, but your mind, on hearing the diagnosis, can manifest the symptoms that match the diagnosis, despite the fact that you are not consciously visualizing this because you don't understand the language or medical jargon. In the same way children can hear a parent say, *I have irritable bowel syndrome*, or *a spastic colon*, or *diverticulitis*, and although children don't understand these words, they can still develop similar or even identical symptoms because they mirror their parents on a level that is above words. Children often resonate on a level that matches their parents' experiences rather than their words.

From the list of scripts below, choose one that is relevant and appealing to you and listen to it or read it every day until your mind is absolutely familiar with it. You may find that you are interested in more than one script. If this is the case, you *must* still focus on one script for twenty-one days then, when you have completed it, move on to another, again for twenty-one days. If you keep interchanging them you will dilute the effect, so concentrate on one script at a time. Later on, when you are listening to the scripts once or twice a month to keep the material in your mind, you can interchange them. You can also create your own script by taking sections from the scripts below and making one that is relevant to you.

Tomorrow, on Day Nine, you will find a further script, number 4, for cell regeneration.

EXERCISE 1

First read through each script to become familiar with each one. Pick the one you like, and record it or write it out so that you can read it to yourself. Pin it up somewhere prominent and begin to memorize it.

---

1. *Script for a younger, healthier body with vitality and energy*
2. *Script for memory and staying mentally young*
3. *Script for weight loss*

1. Script for a Younger, Healthier Body with Vitality and Energy

As you relax and breathe easily your inner mind, the most powerful part of you, is now locking on to these words and accepting them easily as you become more and more aware that you have a strong desire and a powerful motivation and ability to look and feel healthy, vibrant, energetic and younger; to actually become younger.

You are an example of youngness; you express yourself as youth; you embody the expression of youth because you think, act, feel and react as youngness; you feel young and you have a wonderful enthusiasm for life. You are looking forward to your future – there is so much for you to plan and enjoy. Rather than reminiscing about the good old days, you are excited about life today, tomorrow and in the future.

You love life and you love yourself and this is expressed in your zest and enthusiasm for life. You hold in your mind an image of yourself enjoying excellent health, in which you are active and agile; you have vigour and vitality and an abundance of energy that favourably impresses everyone you come into contact with; you are an excellent role model for ageless ageing.

You have a passion for life and embrace new activities without paying any attention to your age. Each day you are moving towards the image of you as energy, vitality, youth and health that you hold in your mind so clearly. You are becoming a walking, talking, breathing example of your image of youth, more so every day. You and your cells are working as a perfect team. As you look after your body, your body looks after you; as you inspire your cells you feel inspired. Your cells are becoming imprinted with your thoughts. You can feel the life force of your cells in every gland, nerve and tissue of your body; you have a constant feeling of rejuvenation.

You are communicating with the intelligence of your cells, directing each cell to function as a young healthy cell now and always.

Every cell in your body is a conscious being; each of your cells is intelligent and responding to you as you think about becoming younger, fitter, active and agile.

Your ability to think these thoughts, to see these things and to accept these suggestions about your health and agility is having a powerful effect on your cells right now. You are able to stimulate your mind and body into action, knowing you don't need to see it specifically – just thinking of it is causing your inner mind to picture it and manifest it perfectly.

Each cell generation is growing strong and resilient and perfect; your cells grow younger and healthier because you instruct them to; your cells replace themselves with even more perfect cells. See your cells now as glowing, healthy, youthful, perfect, radiant, resilient cells, perfectly tuned to other cells, communicating perfectly so every cell is in the right place at the right time, working perfectly for you with perfect results.

You memorize this script rapidly and as you read it or hear it on tape every word is making a deep, lasting impression on your mind and replacing every negative belief with a new constructive one.

2. Script for Memory and Staying Mentally Young

As you relax and absorb these words you are aware that you are making changes in your life, taking vitamins, exercising regularly, and thinking positive thoughts, adopting positive beliefs, which in turn is having an excellent effect on your memory. You are communicating with your brain cells, activating in them an ability and desire to function and perform as perfectly as they did in your youth.

Your memory is becoming better and better. Mentally you are so sharp and agile, you have a wonderful memory, your recall is impressive. You use your mind because your mind is rather like a muscle – the more you use it the better it is. You know that your mind can't wither as long as you keep introducing it to new things. Your mind cannot get old. Your actions combined with your positive and powerful belief system are causing you to have a wonderful, reliable, dependable memory. Everything you hear or see or experience is recorded in your computer-like mind.

Your mind is more efficient than the world's best computer. Like a computer your mind retains information for you, it stores and holds this information for you and you have perfect and instant access to it. You can remember anything, your memory is outstanding, and you have unshakeable confidence and absolute faith in your memory. You never say things like *I have forgotten* or *I can't remember* – instead you say *It will come to me any minute now because I have such a great memory and it always does*. You are running your mind and influencing your memory in the most effective, perfect way.

When you need to remember something, if it does not spring to mind immediately you give an instruction to your computer-like mind to locate the information you need and relay it to you and it always does. You have wonderful recall and retention: you retain information, facts, figures and memories in your mind perfectly and recall them rapidly and accurately. You only need ask your sub-conscious to seek information for you in the same way you would instruct a computer, and within moments the correct information flows into your conscious mind and stays there for as long as you need it.

You keep your mind active and agile by reading a lot, by doing crossword puzzles and brain-teasers, and you get the answers right so easily because you have such a capacity to absorb, retain and recall information. You participate in game shows and quizzes set to test your memory on the radio and in newspapers and magazines – the more you do this the better your memory is.

You read all the time, you love reading, you love exciting your imagination, expanding your mind and using your brain. In Russia they say that a person that no longer reads no longer thinks. They also say that a person who does not read is no better than one who cannot read and that readers are leaders.

You read and, because you have such a good memory, you read even more. Your conscious mind is expanding, retaining more and more information which you can immediately recall. You are able to absorb so much material; things you read, hear or experience are all absorbed into your mind and filed away in a system that is so perfect it delivers this information back to you on demand. You have wonderful powers of concentration, comprehension, retention and recall, and you use them all fully. Whatever you concentrate on you remember. As you get older your memory remains wonderful because you remind yourself daily that everything you see, hear and experience is recorded in your mind for your use. You have a perfect memory and perfect recall: your subconscious mind is a filing cabinet, a computer disc of everything you have ever done and continues to be so throughout your life. You have total faith and absolute confidence in your memory – what is expected tends to be realized, and you expect with supreme confidence that your memory will always be superb and your expectations are met.

You do the things that allow you to maintain a memory that others envy by exercising to ensure that your brain gets a rich supply of oxygen and that the circulation to your brain is good. You pay attention to your digestion and ensure you absorb nutrients which have a positive impact on your brain functions. You take ginkgo biloba because it improves micro-circulation and is excellent for brain function.

Your brain is a self-rejuvenating organ – the more you use it the better it is. As you work out for your body you also work out your brain, memorizing routes, poems, instructions and things that interest and inspire you. You tune in to quizzes on the radio and television and find your brain answering each question so easily and quickly you even impress yourself. Your excellent memory allows you to get older, yet know that you are continually making brain cells and memory cells, and each cell and every neuron and cell receptor is wired up perfectly, resulting in you having a very vital mind. You are mentally young whatever your years, and will continue to be so.

Every time you use the process of saying *It will come to me in a second* it does. Every time you use your technique of imagining your memory working as fast and as accurately as a top of the range computer it does. You radiate confidence in your memory, you exude optimism about your memory.

You memorize this script rapidly and as you read it or hear it on tape every word is making a deep, lasting impression on your mind and replacing every negative belief with a new, constructive one.

3. Script for Weight Loss

As you relax and absorb these words you are aware that you have a strong desire and a compelling ability to become slimmer and leaner. This desire and ability are becoming such a powerful part of you that they overrule any old desire to eat destructively and constantly motivate you to act in ways that cause you to lose excess weight and to become trimmer, healthier, younger and more attractive.

You are now eating healthy, low-fat, fresh food, exercising and looking and feeling younger.

You were born with a perfect body and with a perfect attitude to food. As a baby you were so in tune with your body that you knew when to eat and when to stop eating and you are able to reactivate and reclaim that ability through the power and direction of your inner mind.

You are becoming more and more in tune with your body, working together as a perfect team. You respond to your body by eating healthy, nutritious food that allows your cells to work perfectly and repair damage while slowing down ageing, while your body responds by becoming trimmer, lighter and healthier.

You are so aware that you have a right to be slim, a drive and commitment to be slim, and daily you feel motivated and conditioned to eat differently, to feel different about food. You see food as fuel for your body and cells, and you only want to eat the food that your body can use.

You are freeing yourself for ever from destructive, self-defeating eating habits. There is no room in your mind or body, no room in your life, for over-eating. From now on over-eating is something you used to do, and it cannot, will not, does not influence you any longer as you move on from one great achievement to another, by eating differently, becoming lighter, having more energy, exercising willingly and loving the feeling of fitting into smaller clothes and feeling such a sense of accomplishment and achievement.

You have decided to change your weight, and you easily take

all the action that makes this happen. You are erasing, eliminating and eradicating poor eating habits for ever as you find yourself refusing to eat the type and amount of food that can only harm your body.

You love your body, so you want to take care of it and you always treat it with respect. You choose healthy food and eat less food automatically.

See yourself in your mind at your ideal weight. Feel how lean you are, hear other people praising you on your achievement. Notice how much happier your body is now that you respect it and like it and want to do things that keep it in a healthy, attractive state.

Make an image of how you want to look and tell your mind that this is what you want. As you focus on this image every day you are already moving towards it, because your mind is picking up that your strongest desire is to reach and maintain this size, shape and weight.

You are now a selective and moderate eater. Old eating habits are fading away for ever, leaving you free to eat in a healthy way, leaving you slimmer, more vital, attractive and youthful. Your mind, the most powerful healing force there is, is releasing in you any need to over-eat. You are moving so far, far away from emotional over-eating you can even feel it shrinking, disappearing, going and gone.

As you eat differently your body is becoming a more efficient machine, using the healthy calories you take in to build a perfect body for you and nourishing your cells with natural fruit and vegetables.

Your metabolic rate is increasing through the power and direction of your mind. Feel, believe and imagine your metabolic rate working as perfectly as it did in your childhood. Your stomach is shrinking. Your stomach is the size of your fist, so begin to squeeze your fist while repeating to yourself over and over again: *My stomach is the size of my fist, my stomach is the size of my fist.* Notice your stomach shrinking – feel it becoming smaller now. As you concentrate on this feeling it will increase through the power and direction of your mind. Your stomach is becoming small, tiny, and you find yourself eating enough food to satisfy that capacity of a fist and then stopping easily and willingly because you want to.

From now on you eat only in response to real hunger. You are now and for ever a sensible and selective eater. You drink a lot of water every day to assist your body in eliminating excess weight. You crave water and drink eight glasses a day. Your skin is glowing, you feel fabulous.

You leave some food at every meal because you love that feeling of choice – you always leave something. It makes you feel powerful and healthy. Food cannot control you because you are taking charge of how you eat, how you look and how you feel. You have a positive attitude to your body and a powerful ability to become slim.

You understand that if your body needed excess food it would not turn it into excess body weight. Excess food is wasted wherever it goes. You refuse to treat your body as a dustbin and you leave excess food or throw it away with glee. You know that over-eating is punishing to your body. Your body and cells hate being over-worked with too much food, too much fat, too many additives.

You love your body and it loves you back and is becoming more and more the way you want it to be. You are becoming nourished, filled by the good feelings you have about yourself, and your appetite is changing in the most perfect way. You need less nourishment from food because you are emotionally nourished.

You eat less but you enjoy the food you eat more. You eat slowly, you eat much less fat since you know there is no point in shedding excess fat only to then eat it all back in fatty food. You find fatty, greasy, sugary foods more and more alien to you and you always choose lean, nutritious, healthy food that your body easily digests.

As you eat in this healthy, wonderful way your body uses every calorie to rebuild and rejuvenate you and you become trimmer, slimmer and radiantly healthy. You look younger and fitter – your clothes look so much better on you. Because you feel so good about yourself you exercise and treat your body with love and respect. You easily reach a body weight that is right and appropriate for you, eating healthy, low-fat food; and exercising is becoming a fundamental, integral part of you – it is another way of you being good to yourself, reclaiming a positive self-image and loving yourself.

It is natural for you to eat low-fat, low-sugar food because you are using your power of choice to choose how you are going to feel and look. You have chosen to eat differently and to lose weight easily and permanently. Now get an image of this, and see and feel your stomach as smaller, flatter. Your thighs are leaner, your waist is smaller, because you have made up your mind and set your mind to reach and maintain your ideal weight.

Each of these words makes a deep, vivid and permanent impression on your subconscious. Every day you become more aware of the full, powerful effect these words are having on you. The healing power of your own mind is strengthening and perfecting your ability to change your weight and eating habits. As you absorb this script you are reinforcing your mind, replacing every negative belief with a new, constructive one.

EXERCISE 1
Test for Ageing Successfully

Give yourself one point for each statement to which you can respond *Yes*. Add up your score and read your assessment at the end of this test.

1. I am happy most of the time.
2. I like my body and feel a sense of health and well-being in it.
3. I have a passion for life.
4. I feel young.
5. I am involved in young activities (sport, games, dancing, etc.).
6. I am able to have fun and enjoy doing things without needing to pay any attention to my age.
7. I am able to choose my thoughts and language and to influence how I feel.
8. My identity is completely separate from my age.

9. I do new things and look forward to my future while living in the moment.
10. I change my beliefs to suit my life – I let go of beliefs that are outdated, fixed or rigid.
11. I am flexible in my attitude and opinions.
12. I exercise for at least 30 minutes three times a week and generally enjoy it.
13. I feel energetic after eating.
14. I am within 10 per cent of my ideal weight.
15. I eat real fresh food, drink lots of water and take vitamins and supplements. I eat less fat and fewer meat products, more fish and grains.
16. I don't over-eat or eat late at night very often.
17. My digestion is good.
18. My diet contains lots of fruit and vegetables – at least five servings daily.
19. I am able to limit the amount of alcohol I drink.
20. I consume fewer than two cups of tea and coffee a day.
21. I skin brush and exfoliate regularly.
22. I always use a sunscreen and avoid direct sun.
23. I don't smoke.
24. I don't have any major fears in my life.
25. I breathe properly and enjoy taking deep breaths.
26. Fear of ageing is not something I focus on any longer.
27. I don't use drugs (stimulants, tranquillizers, anti-depressants).
28. I have a happy family life.
29. I get along with people at work and generally.
30. I enjoy friendships.
31. I sleep easily at night for more than six hours without needing pills or alcohol.
32. I wake up feeling refreshed after restful sleep.
33. I sleep with just one flattish pillow.
34. I get to sleep before midnight most nights and before 2 a.m. even more frequently.
35. I restrict electrical appliances in my bedroom and especially around my bed.

36. I feel good about my physical well-being.
37. I feel good about my emotional and psychological well-being.
38. I feel good about my financial well-being.
39. Minor challenges, e.g. traffic jams, being late, missing an appointment, etc., are things I take in my stride.
40. I usually see the positive side of things.
41. I find something to laugh about daily.
42. I am able to laugh at myself.
43. I am not often in a hurry.
44. I can usually control my time rather than it controlling me.
45. I am mentally active – I enjoy reading, writing, keeping up with current affairs, etc.
46. I am flexible and can adjust to changes quite easily.
47. I am not rigid in my thoughts about how things must be. I am open to change, I willingly update my thoughts and beliefs.
48. I can commit myself to a task, job or project.
49. I can commit myself to a relationship.
50. I love my job.
51. I have moments of feeling so happy and carefree.
52. I am able to enjoy silence and calmness on a daily basis, meditating, self-hypnosis, yoga or periods of reflection.
53. I feel very loved.
54. I have a good sex life.

Award yourself one point for every statement to which you respond *Yes*.
Over 45: exceptional.
35–45: excellent.
25–35: good, but pay attention to missing factors to age well.
Under 25: rethink and restructure your priorities by taking action in the areas you answered *No* to.

Take this test again in a few weeks after you have made the lifestyle changes, and you will get a higher score.

TO RECAP

Today, on Day Eight, you have learnt the power of scripts and how something written and put together in a particular format can have an immediate as well as progressive effect on the mind and body. You have learnt more about how to excite and activate your imagination.

You have taken a test that will show you how you are ageing, and by now you will have some very real and definite changes going on in your body, both external and internal.

You can feel proud of yourself for staying with the programme and taking each step. As you begin to see and feel results you will know it was worth it, not just for now but for ten, twenty and thirty years from now when you will still be benefiting.

Thought For The Day
How old would you be if you didn't know how old you are?

Quote
If you were to destroy in mankind the belief in immortality not only love but every living force maintaining the life of the world would at once be dried up.

DOSTOYEVSKY

DAY **9**

How to Reclaim and Redefine Your Image

How Do Cells Work, Why Do They Break Down?

Ageing begins to happen when our system breaks down through free radical damage. Free radicals are rogue cells that contain oxygen in an active form. Oxidation is the combination of oxygen and molecules – unstable molecules are free radicals and are needed to destroy bacteria, parasites and virus-infected cells, but they also damage healthy cells and cause them to malfunction and degenerate. This oxygen-based damage to cells is a major factor in ageing, but it can be counteracted by taking anti-oxidants and by eating foods that are rich in free radical 'scavengers', and by visualizing free radical scavengers surging through the body depleting free radicals.

In the same way that oxidation will rust a car or turn food mouldy it will age our bodies but we can do a lot to slow this down.

Scientists in Kentucky and Oklahoma injected older gerbils with a chemical compound that neutralized the effects of oxygen-based damage to cells, and found that the gerbils began to grow younger. Even their memory reversed to that of younger gerbils. In Dallas similar tests have been done on fruit flies, and the findings have shown that when their cells are protected against oxygen-based damage their lifespan increases by a third.

Scientists at the Biology of Ageing Programme at the National Institute on Ageing in Maryland, USA, believe we could live to 120 if we could prevent the molecular damage going on in our cells. Deepak Chopra, an expert in the field of anti-ageing, said: *If a cell repaired and replaced itself perfectly each time every cell would be perfect and new and we would never grow old.*

Cells have to divide to multiply, and each new cell is encoded with all the information it needs to function perfectly. The number of times a cell replaces itself is very important to ageing. Eventually cells stop reproducing – if they did not do this we actually never would age. By using cell regeneration you can speed up the process of healthy cell replacement, keep your cells in a better, younger condition, and considerably slow down and delay the time when they cease to work to their optimum.

Ageing also begins to occur when cells cease to function at peak efficiency, which in turn leads to a breakdown in cell communication. Once cells stop communicating at peak efficiency all sorts of damage occurs in the body.

Our cells are like miniature factories processing nourishment and voiding waste. The quality of our health relates directly to the quality of the health of our cells. Our cells are constantly replacing themselves, but because of this breakdown in communication a damaged cell will replace itself with a damaged cell, despite the fact that it has the blueprint, the DNA, to replace itself with a perfect cell.

We can reactivate this communication by talking to our cells. It almost sounds too simple, I know, but our cells hear every word we say and already react to these words. Therefore if you were to use a programme whereby you spoke to your cells in a particular format designed to have your cells work better and to continue to communicate with each other, you would be able to prevent much of the breakdown of cell communication and the damage that results from it while keeping your cells working at peak efficiency for longer.

Since our cells respond to our thinking and respond

extremely well to direct mental commands, it is possible to communicate with cells, to talk to them. We already know that our cells hear and respond to our thoughts. Cell regeneration therapy will enable you to communicate with your cells in a much more direct way, you will be able to tell your cells what to do, to command them to work as they are designed to work and to have them act accordingly. This programme will allow you to command and instruct your cells to return to their original blueprint and coding and to function perfectly and properly as they were intended to do.

The mind is able to trigger cell communicators, thus allowing cells to communicate more effectively with each other and, as a result of this, to function more efficiently. Even our immune system responds to our thinking and to our beliefs; it also responds to the way we see our ability to take control of events and will respond as you take control of how you plan to age.

Each cell is capable of replacing itself with a perfect cell for longer, which can considerably delay the onset of ageing. As you listen to the script on cellular regeneration in this chapter, you will be able to communicate with your cells simply by listening to this script on a tape or by memorizing it through a process of reading it frequently.

Every one of your trillions of cells is perfectly able to repair and rejuvenate itself and also to replace itself with a perfect cell. Damaged cells can be programmed to replace themselves with perfect cells because our cells are intelligent and in addition they are directed by an intelligence. Within each cell is the electrical coding that imprints the function and purpose of that cell and is the blueprint for perfect cell replacement.

The mind is stronger than medicine, because our muscles, nerves and cells hear and respond to every word we say, our emotions affect the blood flow and the endocrine system. We can direct our healing intelligence to free, to move, to shrink, to reduce and to minimize ailments and signs of ageing. Cells have an innate intelligence of their own and make decisions below the level of our awareness, and despite the fact that we are not consciously aware of these decisions we nevertheless still have a vast ability to influence them.

Norman Cousins called the placebo the doctor that resides within you. There is a doctor, a chemist, within you that can make the chemicals you need to grow younger, and as you communicate with this 'inner chemist' through cell regeneration therapy you will slow down ageing.

The mind manifests itself through the body, and feelings of joy are transferred from organ to organ, as are feelings of worry, pain or unhappiness. Worry can transform itself into ulcers, throat problems, stomach pains and a host of other ailments; anxiety transfers itself from organ to organ in the body.

The body is very aware of anxiety, and cells hold on to the memory of it and remind you of it through feelings, even when you think you have consciously forgotten it. Feelings of anger stimulate the adrenal glands and the increased adrenaline in the blood causes many changes in the body.

Neuropeptites, which are chemical messengers, travel through the body every time we think a thought or speak a word. Negative thoughts create poisonous neuropeptites, because where a thought goes a chemical goes with it, and where a thought goes energy flows. Neuropeptites and transmitters link up to our thoughts, and all our thoughts turn into molecules. These molecules make decisions within the body that relate to our thoughts, although no one knows yet exactly how this works. When we are rushed, tense and anxious we speed up ageing and become biologically older, whereas when we are calm we slow it down.

If you do something and hate it you will make chemicals which weaken the immune system. If you continuously do something you hate, your body will pay a price for this. Your body will suffer for the fact that you hate what you are doing. If you regularly and consistently do things that you hate you will begin to hate your life. If you do the same thing and love it, you will make very different chemicals which boost the immune system.

We can't always learn to love the things we hate, but we can learn to attach less powerful feelings to them. It is important to accept something and look for some positive aspects of it or to change it. The worst thing we can do is to get into the vicious circle of *I can't accept it and I can't change it* or *I hate this but I have got to do it*.

Believing and saying *I can't accept this and I am unable to do anything about it* will make you feel powerless, and that feeling in turn can even cause your body to feel powerless and to act or behave in a powerless way.

If you feel like this about anything at all, be it your job, how you look or even doing the ironing, then I recommend that you either change how you feel about it and look for some positive aspect of it and decide to feel better about it, or change something about it. Whatever you decide to do, just knowing that you can choose to attach different feelings and language to anything at all will help you.

When I was driving my daughter to school some years ago, the bridge I drove over daily was semi-closed for almost a year, making the journey take three times as long and involving a lot of stationary traffic. After several months of this I noticed I was saying *This is annoying, frustrating, stressful* to myself on a daily basis – I was beginning to hate the journey but I had to drive that route each day. Then I stopped myself, noticed how I was thinking, and decided I must change this, which I did, by reminding myself I had *chosen* this school and *chosen* to drive my daughter every day because it was important to her. I couldn't change the drive to school so I had to change how I felt about it.

I looked at people waiting for the bus and remembered I was lucky to have a car. I don't enjoy being stuck in traffic but I no longer called it stressful, it's just traffic, and I made a point of using that time which I had been thinking of as a waste of time to listen to tapes or have conversations or just think. I even bought myself one of those plastic cup holders that sticks between the seats and made myself some tea which I could enjoy in the car each morning as the traffic crawled along. Something as simple as that made a big difference.

You may say *It's so stressful raising children, commuting to work, dealing with builders, dealing with my boss or my relatives* – the list is endless; and while this may be true it is important to attach less stress to it, to use different words.

The way we define and interpret events affects our cell receptors. It is never what happens but the meaning we attach to it that counts, a negative view of things creates seratonin in our cells and seratonin causes us to feel more pain.

So again, attach a different meaning to ageing – see every stage as challenging and exciting. Attach a different meaning to events that you have perceived as stressful – if you cannot change the event you must change the meaning you attach to it, and by doing something as simple as this you can change your life. Even when you feel there is nothing you can change you can change your thoughts.

What you are seeing as stressful may be someone else's dream come true; they may love to have this stressful experience of being under too much pressure at work, having a car so they could experience traffic or having a family at all.

I took a Russian friend of mine to my local supermarket and she was enraptured by it, she wanted to spend hours looking at all the variety of food and kept saying *You are so lucky, you have so much choice, so much food. You must love coming here, I would like to come here every day*. She attached a very different meaning to being in this shop than did most of the other shoppers, who were looking harassed and wanted to get in and out as quickly as they could.

Deepak Chopra describes going on a rollercoaster ride at a funfair and hating it, finding it scary and making cortisol and adrenaline which can destroy the immune system, or going on that same ride loving it, finding it thrilling and exhilarating and making Interleukin 2, which is the most powerful anti-cancer drug.

A very famous rock star was describing what it was like to

perform on stage and said: *Before I go on stage my heart starts to beat really fast, my palms sweat, adrenaline pumps through me and I feel so excited I can't wait to go out there and perform.*

Compare this with another famous performer, who gave up performing live after describing this. *When I was about to go on stage awful things started happening to my body. I would get a rapid heart beat, adrenaline would rush through me, I would feel sweaty and nervous and realized I was having panic attacks; eventually I had to give up live performances because they would not go away.*

The feelings and sensations are so similar but the interpretation is completely different and the chemicals each performer manufactured would be different because of these opposite interpretations.

If you use ageing language, if your identity of yourself is as old or ageing, then your DNA will pass on through each cell generation the belief that you are old or ageing.

The same is true with weight and addictions. If your language and thoughts are all along the lines of *I can't lose weight, I can't eat like other people do* then you are passing on that information from one cell to the next.

Because cells remember addictions, weight patterns, anxieties and pass this information on through each cell generation, the memory of the addiction, weight, etc. can persist in new cells even years later. By using cell regeneration therapy you can change this for ever.

The worst beliefs are the kind that say *Other people can do that but I can't, other people can look younger, but I can't.* You can, but first you must believe that you can, so that your cells are able to believe that you can.

Your cells are not able to disagree with you and accept everything you say and even think as a fact, so you have nothing to lose and everything to gain by telling yourself and your cells the opposite. Tell yourself you look and feel ageless every day and you will become ageless.

Our bodies are run by a labyrinth, an organization of intelligence with information continuously being sent out and received, and by using relaxation methods, the power of thought and visualization techniques we can go deep enough to positively influence this organization of intelligence, to change body patterns and influence cells so we can enjoy better health and longevity.

In my practice as a hypnotherapist I have been doing this for years, going on a journey into the body with my patients communicating with their cells and activating the body's ability to heal and repair itself, especially with patients who have had chronic illnesses. Some of the results have been outstanding.

I then began to study the effects this technique, which I call 'cell regeneration therapy', had on ageing and they were equally impressive. I travelled across America studying with experts in the ageing process and gathering information for this book.

In the West we have been taught to hand over our bodies and our ailments to the medical profession and we give them the responsibility for making us well, and yet we have more power to heal, to fix and to change our bodies than any outside source.

Doctors can do wonderful work especially in the area of surgery, but in the area of healing the body you can make the healing chemicals needed, you only need to be shown how to do it. Your body can heal and repair itself in many areas and can slow down and arrest ageing.

A case has been documented of a teenager who lost her heel in a motorbike accident and using a form of hypnosis commanded her body to grow a new left heel, using the right heel as a model and she did, she successfully regrew her heel.

Healthy tissue has been regrown and burns healed without scarring using the same process. What you think is possible affects your body.

Deepak Chopra says: *We can interrupt the past pattern of ageing at a cellular level, then the DNA can work its miracles, our intelligence is so willing to provide this.*

EXERCISE 1

Practise using the mind to trigger cell communicators, so that the cells are strong and communicate perfectly with each other. Read through the script on cell command therapy, then close your eyes and visualize all your cells in the right place at the right time doing their perfect work.

Communicate with your cells today, to activate their ability to repair, renew and replace themselves at peak efficiency. Talk to them and tell them what you want and expect from them. You can talk to your cells the way you might talk to a very bright 10-year-old child, giving them clear and easy-to-follow instructions, telling them how you want them to behave. Tell your cells to behave in a way that will allow you to stay young. Remember and refer to everything you learnt on Day Six about how to programme your mind, and apply these same rules to programming your cells. As I mentioned earlier, your cells are like smart children – they know *exactly* what to do to allow you to remain young and they know *exactly* how to do it, but they have to be commanded, instructed and told what to do in a specific way that causes them to respond to you. Some of my clients really dislike the word *command*, and I have to remind them that I am not commanding *them*, no one is bossing *them* about, but if they wish to they can command their own body cells to work more productively for them. The key is to use the points below as you communicate with your cells and any other part of you.

1. Talk to your cells in the present tense, and only use positive words. Say *Grow younger and healthier, replace yourself with even more perfect cells*, rather than *Don't be old or sick*.
2. Be absolutely clear – show your cells with words and images exactly how you want them to be.
3. Use very descriptive words like *glowing*, *healthy*, *youthful*, *perfect*, *radiant*, *resilient*. Tell your cells they are perfectly tuned to other cells, communicating perfectly, so every cell

is in the right place at the right time, working perfectly with perfect results.

4. Use the present tense as you talk to your cells, and a progressive form of conditioning. For example, *My cells are becoming stronger, each cell generation is strong, resilient and perfect.*

5. Be as detailed as you can. It is OK to be vague about something you can't fully comprehend. For instance, because I like being slim I tell my cells and metabolic rate to act as they did when I was a child. I tell my digestion to do the same thing, and it behaves much better. I don't really know what that looks like, nor do I need to – I just tell my cells to do the work. I tell them how much it means to me and I thank them, imagine it a little, then leave it to them to do it.

6. Communicate with your cells frequently. It is better to spend five minutes communicating with them every day than one hour every ten days.

---

4. Script for Cell Regeneration Therapy and Younger Skin

How to bring about repair of body tissues as a result of direct mental commands

As you relax your inner mind, the most powerful part of you, is now locking on to these words and accepting them easily, as you become more and more aware that you have a strong desire and a powerful motivation and ability to look and feel younger, to become younger, and to have younger skin and a younger, healthy complexion.

You are now ready and able to motivate your skin cells to act like younger cells. You have the power to influence your cells to communicate with any part of your body and to have that part respond to your instructions.

You are now using the power of your mind, directing and commanding your skin cells to act like younger cells.

Because your body is controlled by a network of intelligence which is influenced by your mind, you are able to relax deeply enough to influence your own mind, to change patterns of the body and to slow down the ageing process.

You are able to accept only positive ideas about your cells and to imprint this on to them.

You are communicating with the intelligence of your cells, directing each cell to function as a young healthy cell now and always.

Every cell in your body is a conscious being. Each of your cells is intelligent and responds to you as you think about becoming younger.

Imagine that you can influence cell renewal so that it speeds up and becomes more efficient, and as a result of this, ageing slows down. Your ability and willingness to talk to your cells is slowing down ageing.

When you were younger your cells repaired and renewed themselves at peak efficiency. You had perfect cells and your cells have a perfect memory of this.

You are able to activate this memory and to set off changes in your cells just by thinking of it. Think of your cells becoming younger now, imagine your cells doing their perfect work at peak efficiency. Imagine and feel your cells performing more effectively so that your skin functions as a younger skin does and will continue to do so. Every time you think these thoughts, each cell is renewing itself with a younger, healthier and stronger cell.

As you relax and think these thoughts or hear these words, you are able to drift into a different state of consciousness, a state where you are able to penetrate the cell wall, to communicate with your DNA, the blueprint for healthy cells.

You are responding wonderfully to direct mental commands and enabling each cell to replace itself with a younger, more healthy cell, activating the rejuvenating process by communicating with your cells and increasing cell renewal and regeneration.

Your thoughts are commanding your skin to perform at peak efficiency as it did in your youth.

Since whatever you focus on you move towards, you are focusing on your connective tissue as supportive, imagining that oxygen-rich blood is being sent by your subconscious mind to your skin to feed and nourish it, to feed the cells and increase cell renewal even more.

You know that your beliefs create biology, that your thoughts are so powerful that they are creating physical effects within your body right now.

You are activating healthy cells through the power of your thinking. As you relax and take in these words, know that your mind responds to your thinking, to the words and images you make.

See your skin as resilient, more supple and elastic, able to heal and repair itself quickly.

Sebum is increasing, your epidermis is remaining thick, and your sebaceous glands are staying active. Your connective tissue is strong and your skin's immune response cells work perfectly. Your healing white blood cells are working as perfectly as they did in your childhood.

Your skin cells are regaining and retaining their ability to communicate perfectly with each other so that each cell is able to do its work perfectly. Your cell production is increased, surface cells are being shed more quickly, new cells are rapidly coming to the surface, and with this rapid turnover of skin cells your skin looks and feels younger, moist, glossy and healthier.

By frequently focusing on this you are activating your skin cells and speeding up cell renewal, so that your skin has lustre, glow and a smoother, younger appearance.

Through cellular communication you are speeding up production of collagen and elastin and encouraging your skin's natural repair process.

Imagine now the surface dead skin cells being shed – see them falling away as dead dry flakes, as dust. As this happens, new, healthy, glossy cells are constantly moving up from the dermis like perfectly organized ranks to the skin's surface. You are constantly producing healthy glowing cells – your skin looks moist, supple, younger, more healthy. Your complexion is clear and glossy.

In younger skin, surface cells are shed every twenty-eight days, so imagine, instruct and command your cells to shed every twenty-eight days, revealing new, healthy, younger skin.

The dull, dead cells are falling away. Imagine the protein bonds that held the dead cells on the surface like glue responding perfectly to your thoughts and freeing up to discard the old cells.

When you exfoliate you see improved results. Your moisturizer works better at protecting your consistent supply of healthy, glossy, plump, moist, firm young cells. Your skin quality is smoother, firmer, more youthful. Your body cells act as younger cells. Your supportive network of collagen and elastin fibres are also strong and remain so.

Even thinking about their strength can increase it, so see your network of collagen and elastin becoming stronger, leaving your skin supple with a smooth surface.

Through your imagination and through your creative thinking you are directing your sebum production, ensuring that it is speedy and constant. As a result your skin looks and feels more moist. Your sebaceous glands stay active to keep your skin moist and you are able to encourage this by visualizing it.

Now think, see and believe in your mind's ability to increase circulation and cell respiration so that even now your cells are repairing themselves, communicating productively, and producing plenty of collagen to help your skin's support system. You help your skin even more by constantly removing negative thoughts and language about ageing from your thinking and from your mind.

Your mind is influencing your body and you are influencing your mind in the most perfect way. You are developing a clear mental image, visualizing your skin and skin cells as young and healthy, knowing that the more you imagine it the more rapidly it will occur.

Your ability to think these thoughts, to see these things and to accept these suggestions about your skin is having a powerful effect on your cells right now. You are able to stimulate your mind and body into action. Remember, you don't need to see it specifically – just thinking of it is causing your inner mind to picture it and manifest it perfectly.

Because your imagination has no limits you can see and feel your skin as younger, your muscles as tighter and firmer, any lines as finer. As you do this you are reinforcing your subconscious mind, replacing negative thoughts with new, positive ones. As you focus on achieving younger skin, with confidence in your ability to make it happen, you can and will achieve it.

This image of you with younger, firmer skin is becoming more real, more attainable, and more clear each time you hear this script. Your inner mind, the most powerful part of you, is locking on to these words, hearing them over and over again. They are becoming a powerful part of your memory.

Your skin has a natural ability to renew itself and is doing so every second. You make a new epidermis every month, so see your epidermis replacing itself with a new, thicker epidermis full of healthy cells ready to do their work perfectly, enabling your skin to retain optimum elasticity.

Now see your skin healing and replenishing itself easily, while you make more epidermal skin cells nourished with nutrient-laden blood. Your blood capillaries are strong and healthy, aiding blood flow to the skin.

You are stimulating your circulation and maximizing production of new cells by breathing properly and deeply. As you breathe deeply you are increasing the amount of oxygen available to your cells and the elimination of toxins. You are also strengthening your cells and rejuvenating your body while increasing your skin's cycle of cell reproduction, so that plump, light-reflecting cells come to the surface more frequently.

The bonds that held dead cells on the skin's surface are broken easily, revealing a fresh skin that looks hydrated and healthy. Your skin is continually behaving as a young skin does, making collagen and elastin, staying smooth, supple, elastic and firm. Your facial muscles stay strong and work well, supporting your skin.

Every cell in your body is now more perfect, more youthful, more alive. Each cell is replacing itself with a purer, finer, more perfect cell. Dead skin flakes fall away, encouraging new layers of skin cells to form and show as rapidly as they do in younger skin.

Your skin is looking fresher, newer – proof that it is renewing itself at a faster, younger rate. Your complexion is smooth, glossy, youthful and luminous. As you successfully use the power of your mind for cellular regeneration, cell communicators are triggered, leaving your skin moist and satiny with improved skin tone.

Visualize free radical scavengers working perfectly effectively to destroy free radicals. See these free radical scavengers mopping up free radicals and minimizing any free radical damage so that your skin cells are strong, resilient, and communicate and work perfectly with each other, giving out and receiving the right information.

Your trillions of cells are all in the right place at the right time, doing the right job – boosting cell renewal, protecting the cell membrane, promoting healthy cell division, and activating DNA. A wonderful skin quality is the result.

You have perfect cell protein collagen and elastin, your skin is supported and strong. Now see your muscles as strong. Your facial muscles are attached to your skin – see your muscles as taut, your skin as firm.

You have excellent circulation, good skin tone and colour, excellent blood and lymph flow, and cells that are rich in oxygen and nutrients. Your muscles act as a support system for your skin. See your muscles as supple and firmer, as they were in your youth. On top of your muscles see healthy connective tissue. Next is the dermis and the epidermis, which is thick and healthy because it is full of growing cells.

Your skin is firm and supported. New collagen is always forming. Every cell is surrounded by connective tissue and you see this as elastic, supple, firm, with a healthy blood supply, keeping your muscles young and elastic.

Because you care about your skin you have a strong desire to keep it in excellent condition, so you eat a healthy diet, rich in vitamins and anti-oxidants that guard against cell destruction. You drink eight glasses of water daily, vital for healthy skin. You breathe properly. You use sunblock and the best skincare routine for you. You exercise for healthy bones and organs.

Each night your cells renew and repair themselves as you sleep, so you feel this and see this happening as you fall asleep. You focus on and dream of your healthy cells renewing and repairing and taking care of your skin.

As you sleep your subconscious mind is increasing blood flow to your skin, affecting your skin and skin cells, affecting you in the most perfect way. You are producing healthy hormones, enabling your skin to function as a young, healthy skin. Your cells are becoming super-efficient.

These words are influencing your cells and influencing you in the most positive, safe way, allowing you to achieve younger-looking and younger-functioning skin.

Exercise to Reclaim and Redefine the Image of Yourself

One of the best ways to have healthy cells is to have a healthy attitude to yourself and to truly love your body. It is not good enough to love only a part of your body, the parts that you like and accept or feel are your best features – you must love all of it, since if you reject any part of you then you are ultimately rejecting yourself. This rejection of the self is expressed in the cells in a negative way, whereas when you accept and love every part of you your cells feel loved, appreciated and valued and act accordingly. Again I realize this almost sounds too simple to be believable, but it is true. Your body mirrors what is going on in your mind, and your cells mirror what you feel about yourself by behaving in a way that matches the feeling.

In order that you have healthy cells, we are going to begin the process by focusing on all the positive things about you.

We are often uncomfortable about focusing on what is good about ourselves and quick to focus on what we think is wrong with us. In fact many people seem to feel easier criticizing themselves, saying *I look awful in this, I look old, fat, tired*, and so on, yet when they are given a compliment they can actually become uncomfortable. For example:

You look nice.	*What, in this old thing?*
Your hair looks nice.	*No, it can't do – it needs washing.*
That's a nice dress.	*Oh, it's so old – I've had it for years.*
You did really well today.	*Oh, it was nothing really.*

We must learn to take compliments more easily. This will only happen as we give ourselves more compliments and begin to see all the good things that are part of us, not the opposite.

We can always find whatever we look for. If you look for what is negative about yourself you can find something, and if you look for what is positive you can find something. You must learn to look for what is good and positive about you, about your appearance, your age and your character.

It is lovely to be given a compliment, and it can make us feel great when someone says something nice about us; however, there is a big difference between liking compliments and actually needing them in order to feel good about ourselves. If you always need compliments it will make you needy, which is not a good state to be in. Giving yourself compliments regularly will move you to a better state.

Give yourself a lot of compliments and praise yourself a lot – it will raise your self-esteem massively – and compliment people around you as well, because not only will it make them feel good, it will have a good effect on you. One of the most rapid and easiest ways to raise our self-esteem is to raise the self-esteem of others, to praise and compliment others. Obviously it must be genuine, but it is so easy to find something nice to say about someone else and you will grow in the most beneficial way if you start doing this.

The old school of thought says that praising people makes them big-headed and arrogant, whereas criticism stops them getting above themselves. This is just not true. Criticism withers people, while praise makes them grow, so praise more and criticize less, especially with yourself. Again, you can only change yourself. This book is about you making changes for you, so praise yourself more, criticize yourself less, stop saying *Oh, I'm so stupid, I can't believe I did that, I'm an idiot, I'm an old fool, I look horrible, I'm too fat, too old* – find out all the good things about you and focus on them.

If you occasionally find yourself saying *I did something stupid* change it to *I made a mistake*. We all make mistakes, and if you lapse into criticizing yourself, just decide not to believe it. I do this if I get lost on a journey or I get delayed – it is so easy to say *I can't believe I didn't look up the route before I left* or *I'm so dumb for not leaving earlier*. Although I can't remember when I last spoke to myself like that, if I do, I decide not to believe what I am saying and instead I tell myself it's OK to get lost, it's all right to be late occasionally. I don't allow myself to believe any pointless criticism, including my own, although constructive criticism has a value.

Of course you may have experiences of people who seem very arrogant and full of themselves and put you off the idea of self-praise; however, people who come across as truly arrogant usually don't actually believe in themselves very much at all. They are the opposite end of the same scale to people who lack confidence. So they put on a show of confidence not just to convince others but to convince themselves.

People who truly like themselves have no need to do this. You can be quietly confident, you can radiate inner confidence, you can believe in yourself, and you can do all of this for you, for your own benefit. If you believe you are ageless, beautiful and wonderful you won't feel the need to convince others of the same – it just won't be necessary – yet by putting a higher value on yourself you will automatically increase the value that other people have of you. If you increase your self-image, others will too.

The most important and the most powerful words you will ever hear are the words you say to yourself and believe. The most important opinion for you is your opinion.

I learnt long ago that the best thing to do is to pay no attention to flaws, because no one else notices them or notices them to the degree that you do. People tend to see us the way we see ourselves, they pick up the way we feel about ourselves because our self-image reflects out from us to the people we are around, who then reflect it back to us. If you cease to notice minor flaws, no one else will pay them much attention either, but if you go on and on about them you only draw attention to something you want to go unnoticed.

Sometimes we dislike a part of ourselves for no valid reason. When I was younger I had a real complex about my legs. They were so skinny, and all the boys at school used to call me Twiglet, because I guess that's what they thought my legs looked like. Luckily my grandmother told me it was a compliment, so it bothered me a little less, although out of school I never ever wore skirts and lived in trousers. I was dating a guy from outside my school when I was 16, and was working as a waitress in a restaurant on Saturdays. One day he came in to see me unexpectedly and I remember standing behind a table, because I was so determined he would not see my legs in the skirt that was part of the uniform. I went on and on about how thin they were, and he picked up my belief system and eventually agreed with me.

I'm not sure when I began to think differently, but I do remember my next boyfriend telling me I had the best legs he had ever seen. When I was an exercise teacher many of the girls in my class used to say, *If I do your class can I get legs like yours?* I had an article written about me in *Marie Claire*, and they very nicely wrote: *Marisa has the kind of legs that make you ponder on life's injustices.*

So somewhere in between hating my legs and being extremely self-conscious of them I grew to love them and see them as an asset, and many times I was told I had wonderful legs. This wasn't because they changed as I got older – they are still exactly the same legs, but I felt different about them. My legs have never changed shape or size but I have changed from hating them and feeling self-conscious and embarrassed about them to loving them.

When you are able to do this about every part of your body, you will feel so different, and this different expression and feeling about yourself will cause your cells to pick up positive feelings about you and thrive instead of wither.

Sometimes, though, I still get told my legs are too skinny, but once I had begun to like them I didn't really care what anyone else said because I was happy with them and had accepted them. I was crossing the road in London once and a man came up to me and said: *Your legs are like matchsticks*. I was able to burst out laughing and reply: *Your brain is made of the same material*. Only unattractive men have come up to me to tell me my legs are too thin; it is interesting and amazing that they seem to feel it is OK to comment on my body, but I have come to realize that the people who criticize us always have the most criticism reserved for themselves.

Critical people simply reflect out their own self-criticism. It is as if they have to make everyone else aware of any faults or flaws so that they don't feel alone in their negative self-judgement; they seem to need us all to feel as bad about part of ourselves as they secretly do about themselves, then they can feel more comfortable – something to do with safety in numbers. Critical people have the most criticism reserved for themselves, so when they criticize someone else they are really describing their own world and talking in a paradox. Gorky said: *A miserable man must find a more miserable man, then he is happy*.

So if you are around people who criticize you, refuse to absorb it. Only people who feel mediocre criticize, superior people praise. As you cease to criticize yourself and others you will feel quite different, and your cells will become a real and physical expression of this different and positive feeling. It helps to remind yourself and the critic that critical people, who focus on others' flaws, are usually so aware of their own – they feel deep down that they are not good enough and seem to need to make everyone else aware of their flaws so that we will also feel not good enough and keep them company. They may only feel equal to you if they criticize you.

Walking along the road a few years ago, a man shouted out of his car to me: *Those legs should be up there on billboards*, while days later another shouted out: *Sparrow legs*. So which should I believe? Whichever I choose to believe or want to believe, is the answer.

I went on a date once with a man I had met at a party. I was wearing Levi's when we met, and when he took me out to lunch I had on a skirt. I saw him the next day and he said to me, *When you turned up at my office I thought you had such thin legs you looked a bit skinny, but when I got back to my office my colleagues said, 'Who was that girl you were with? She had fantastic legs.'* It was interesting that he changed his opinion of me because his friends influenced him.

People are very easily influenced – fashion shows us that. We don't feel comfortable wearing something that is judged unfashionable or dated, although in its moment of fashion we loved it – once it is judged no longer fashionable we are embarrassed to be seen in the garment. Of course the garment has not changed, but we have changed our opinion and become influenced by fashion. We are also very influenced by fashion not just in clothes but in furniture, food, music, and so on. We are all easily influenced, but unaware that we have the power to influence how we feel about ourselves and consequently how everyone else feels about us.

When I was teaching exercise classes in Chicago, one of my fellow teachers was small and quite muscular and yet she had a fantastic body image. She would always say during her class: *I love my legs, they are strong and they carry me around, they are so good to me; I love my body because it takes care of me so well.* She never compared herself to anyone or said *I wish I looked like that*, she didn't ever complain about her body but always praised it and acknowledged it, she accepted herself and taught herself to feel great about her looks and herself. She obviously made an impression on me, because I have never forgotten her.

I also have a friend who has the most amazing, perfect body. I asked her once what it was like to have such a body, since I imagined it must be wonderful and that she would be free of all complexes and she would feel lucky and proud. Certainly all her friends envied her.

She answered: *My body is a curse to me and it always has been. Men stare at me and make me feel uncomfortable, they only want to get to know me because they love my body and I hate it.* I was stunned by her response and learnt a lot from it. I have since noticed how many of my most attractive clients (some of them truly beautiful models and actresses) have as many if not more complexes about how they look than the plainer ones who want to lose weight or look better.

This is because they are always comparing themselves with someone else whom they see as prettier or younger. It is such a waste – you cannot compare yourself with anyone because you are unique. Beauty is not just in the eye of the beholder, it is in our eyes. How we see ourselves is reflected out to the world, and we can choose to see ourselves in a positive light and so will everyone else. Our partners don't really care if we are a few pounds overweight – they probably don't even notice – but if you go on about it they *will* notice and may begin to feel about it the way you do.

If you share your life with people who criticize your appearance, remind yourself that they are insecure about themselves. By all means make changes that will allow you to feel better, but do it for you.

We can change any belief about ourselves. You don't have to look like a model to appreciate yourself, you don't have to be young to have value. Real beauty comes from within. Learn to love every bit of yourself and see a value in your body – wrinkles are character lines, stretch marks left by being lucky enough to have children.

Don't get caught in the trap of saying *I hate my nose or my stomach, my thighs or my face.* If you can change some body parts through diet and exercise, by all means do that, and if you can't change a part of yourself, accept it and look for some positive aspects of it. The worst thing we can do is to fall into the trap of believing and saying *I can't accept it and I can't change it. I hate this part of me and I can't do anything about it.*

Barbra Streisand has a large nose that has never detracted from her beauty, and all around us are examples of men and women who are not at all perfect but who believe in themselves with such conviction that others believe in them as well. I was very struck by the model Heather Mills, who lost a leg in a motorcycle accident yet continued to model, went on television to show her prosthesis, got married, and inspired us all with her positive self-image.

When my little girl was 5 she was in the bath and said to me *Mummy, I hate my hair. It's too curly. I hate my mouth and I hate my body.* I couldn't believe that my baby, who has always been brought up to think positively, had already begun to have such a negative body image. Her two best friends were Japanese, and I had told them how pretty they were and what beautiful shiny straight hair they had. When I took them out people would often say how pretty and well-behaved they were, and my daughter decided she wanted to be like Misaki and Yuki and was comparing herself to them unfavourably.

So I said to her: *Tell me what you do like about you first. Let's talk about what you love about you.* And she reeled off a list, starting with her eyes, her teeth, her smile, her skin. She immediately began to feel better about herself, and as the list got longer she forgot to be negative.

When she says, *Mummy, do I look pretty in this?* I always say, *What do you think you look like?* and she always says, *Oh, I think I look gorgeous.* And I tell her that is what counts, what you think you look like matters most of all, but I tell her she's gorgeous too, I want her to believe in herself.

She would come home from school and say, *X said I am ugly.* I would reply, *Do you think you are ugly?* She would answer, *No,*

I know I am not ugly, so I would ask her how she knew she wasn't ugly and why she would pay any attention to someone else, who was only trying to upset her. We must all learn to value our own opinions more than those of someone else who may not have our best interests at heart.

When I was little my relatives all used to say, *Aren't you tall, aren't your feet big?* I remember so much longing to be petite, because they didn't say, *Aren't you tall* in a positive way. It's so easy to get a complex. In fact I love being tall, and my feet are size five, but when I was nine I worried that I would grow into a giant because people commented on my height in a way that made me feel negative about it and conscious of it.

I refused to have my photograph taken for years because I hated the way I looked. Years later, when I looked at photos of myself as a child, I was surprised that I was cute because I felt ugly, but of course these feelings weren't based on anything real or rational – they very rarely are.

I see this with so many of my clients who have a very negative self-image when they look absolutely fine, and although I could tell them they look wonderful, my job is to make them absolutely believe and feel they look wonderful, that they are wonderful and unique and cannot be compared with anyone else. If we feel negative and get criticized it can hurt; if we feel positive we can let it go.

The most important thing is to like yourself, to learn to love every part of you. We cannot amputate parts of ourselves, we have to learn to accept them and look for the positive. In this section you are going to acknowledge yourself in the most positive way, to focus on all the things you like about yourself and to make this list longer and much more significant than any negative list you may have. We will do this with your looks, your age and your personality.

At the end of this section you are going to make a list of all the good things about yourself. As you make this list, remember that every cell of your body hears and responds to the words and feelings you have about yourself. The more you criticize your body the more despondent it becomes; the more you praise it the more it reacts to your praise. If you praise your body more and more it will change and function much better, as well as looking and feeling better.

You have a mind within each and every one of your trillions of body cells, and these cells, unlike brain cells, have no ability to doubt what you tell them. They accept your words and opinions as the absolute truth. By making your words, opinions and thoughts more and more positive, you can change your emotional and physical body. Happy thoughts quite literally make happy cells. When you are feeling happy and feeling good about yourself, every cell in your body is an expression of this feeling. When you are feeling dissatisfied with yourself, every cell in your body is an expression of this feeling too.

As you tell your body and yourself how wonderful you look, how wonderful your body is at taking care of you, at performing daily miracles that keep you alive, your body will physically respond to these words in the most positive way.

BUPA recently ran a series of very successful adverts that focused on all the miracles of the human body. The heading of each advert was: *You are a miracle, we want to keep you that way*. You are indeed a miracle – the human body does so many amazing things, and by thinking this way, by focusing on the wonderful things your body does for you daily, and thanking it and acknowledging it instead of criticizing it, your body will respond to you and you can remain a miracle and look, feel and remain younger throughout your life.

Imagine if your body was a person – how do you think it would feel if you said, *I hate my body* or *How could anyone love this old body?* or *I hate my stomach or my legs* on a regular basis? It would feel despondent and would feel like giving up and not bothering, since it is so unappreciated; your cells would become a physical expression of the despondency. This can and does happen within the body – the more you love your body the more lovable it will become to you and the more it will respond to you.

We have receptor sites in the body, including the liver, kidneys, bone marrow and immune system, that respond to our thoughts, so a form of communication or interplay is always going on between the mind and the body. When you feel despair or hate parts of yourself, your body responds to this feeling of giving up by giving up with you, by not bothering to make the healing chemicals you need to thrive because your body has to express the same despair that is going on silently in your mind.

You are making a very different body when you are happy or feeling joy; you are also making a very different body when you are at peace with yourself. Your body chemistry or bio-chemistry will be very different to that of someone who is unhappy with themselves. Bernie Siegal gives a great example of this in his book *Love, Medicine and Miracles*, when he talks about the tests that have proved lovers are more resistant to poisons because their immune system is so good. In that state of being loved they feel cherished, valued and appreciated.

Good relationships always help us, which is why people who have them generally live longer and are healthier. From today you are going to have a good relationship with yourself and to cherish, value and appreciate yourself.

Start now to love your body, to love everything about it, and you will very quickly notice how much better it performs for you. Begin to credit your body rather than discredit it; instead of complaining about what it won't do or has not done, see all the excellent things it does for you. As you re-evaluate your body in a positive way, it will respond positively to this re-evaluation.

I also recommend that you take a few moments and apologize to your body for all the negative things you have thought and said about it, and make a decision not to do this any more.

EXERCISE 2

Remember every compliment you have ever been given for what you are, what you do, how you look, and so on – now start writing all these compliments into your workbook. Write out every one of these compliments.

Now add to the list by complimenting yourself on how you look.

Work through your body from head to toe, complimenting yourself on your hair, your eyes, your skin, your smile, your body, the way you move, how nice you always smell, how infectious your laugh is, and so on.

Thank your body for looking after you, for taking care of you so well.

As you appreciate your body it will become more appreciable to you, so get into the habit of appreciating yourself every day.

Repeat these statements to yourself, and as you do, feel and imagine your body getting the message.

As you make each statement out loud, feel as if it is true right now.

Repeat the following statements out loud, feeling as if it is all true this instant. Say

My body is ageless.

My body is graceful.

I have shiny, bright, lovely eyes and they see the beauty in me and in everyone else.

My hair is shiny and glossy and healthy and always smells lovely.

My teeth allow me to eat anything I wish.

I have a beautiful smile.

My skin is soft and lovely to touch.

My hands are such an asset to me, what would I do without them?

My body is a miracle – it digests food, combines it with oxygen from the air I breathe, and builds a perfect body for me.

I love my body, I love myself.

My memory is great — I can remember so many things. I have a wonderful mind and a wonderful brain.

I have a great heart, powerful lungs, muscles that take care of me, a good nervous system, a strong immune system, legs that take me anywhere I want to go.

I am a wonderful dancer.

I have a beautiful voice.

TO RECAP

Today, on Day Nine, you have learnt all about cells and the role they play in ageing.

You have learnt that you have the power and ability to talk to your cells as easily as you might talk to a friend, to give your cells clear instructions in the way you want them to behave and to have that behaviour begin.

You have learnt what happens when you criticize yourself or hate parts of you, and the very real and negative effect this has on your body.

You have learnt how to understand and deal with critical people.

You have learnt to reclaim yourself as a beautiful and wonderful person.

You have learnt that the most important compliments and opinions are your opinions about you and that you have full power to influence them in a truly positive way.

You now have a programme for cellular regeneration that you can listen to or refer to daily.

Thought For The day
You are a walking, talking, living expression
of your beliefs.

Quote
Whatever you can do, or dream you can,
begin it.
Boldness has genius, magic and power in it.
Begin it now.

GOETHE

PART THREE

Action

Action Day

Changing Your Lifestyle and Habits

Over the last nine days you have done some very powerful work to change your concept of ageing and to change the way you are ageing. You have changed your thoughts, your beliefs, your language and your physiology and reclaimed a positive self-image. Today, on Action Day, we are going to cover changing your lifestyle and changing your habits.

Lifestyle is very important, and making lifestyle changes that allow you to have a better lifestyle can increase your life by at least ten years and can even add fifty years to your life. Your body can quite literally grow younger instead of growing older if you treat it the right way, whereas a lifestyle of bad habits can reduce your lifespan by forty years.

I have spent most of this book focusing on changing your thinking, your attitudes and your beliefs, and I have told you numerous times by now that that is the most important thing of all, that making changes in what you think and believe can and will change how you age.

Now we are moving on to another equally important section of the book, and if you believed up until now that all you had to do was change your thinking, and now feel disappointed that you have to make lifestyle changes as well, let me reassure you.

Changing your thinking is the most important step, which is

why it is Step One. Does that mean that in theory you could think positively, live a destructive lifestyle and stay younger? In theory you may very well be able to do this, but you have bought this book because you want to become younger, you want to grow up to ten years younger in ten days, and you want to hold on to looking and feeling younger than you are chronologically, throughout your life. If you are serious about wanting to become younger, to live longer, to look and feel younger at any age (and it is such a great subject to be serious about), then it is absolutely worth making lifestyle changes as well, especially since the ones in this book are easy to make.

If you want to become younger, and you follow the nine steps that take you up to today, but you live on junk food, never exercise and sleep close to a lot of electricity, you will deny yourself the full and wonderful results you could achieve. Why settle for anything less than results of 100 per cent?

I am very aware that many books that promote lifestyle changes fail because they are too rigid and sell you a lifestyle that you may not be able to maintain. With this in mind, I have developed a chapter of easy lifestyle changes that give you a lot of choice, a lot of flexibility, and a lot of say in the changes you make.

Since 95 per cent of what we do is habit and is automatic, it follows that changing even some of these habits is going to make a bit impact on our ability to age successfully. What you begin and repeat over and over will become a new habit, a habit that has lasting and visible benefits. By taking action today you can make anti-ageing a new habit and part of a new and enriching lifestyle for you.

It is important not to get stuck in a rut or an outdated routine, since that in itself is very ageing. If you want to stay young, learn something new. It may be said that an old dog can't learn new tricks, but humans can learn something new at any age because they have the ability to be flexible in attitudes and beliefs. You don't even need to work at eliminating old habits – you can simply replace them with new ones.

When I lived in Cambridge I saw some graffiti outside one

of the colleges that said: *If you aren't part of the solution you are part of the problem.* I think this is very appropriate in the field of ageing and anti-ageing.

Over the next few pages you will discover the anti-ageing properties of Diet, Vitamins, Supplements, Digestion, Exercise, Skin Brushing – even the way you sleep and the amount of electricity you are near. I have written each section in a way that gives you masses of choice – you can choose which wonderfoods to include in your diet, which vitamins and supplements to take.

You will be given a list of things that will allow you to maintain good digestion, which is so linked to good ageing, and a list that shows you how to limit easily and effectively the amount of electricity your body is exposed to, especially when you sleep, as well as learning the anti-ageing properties of correct sleep.

You will also learn the benefits of exercise in limiting bone and muscle loss while maintaining agility and energy and hormone levels, and you will learn the wonderful and immediate benefits of skin brushing.

After you have finished reading this section on actions to take to become younger, you will find your final exercises for the day.

Today, Day Ten, is so important, so enter into it with the belief and commitment that you are going to make wonderful changes and that this day of change is one you will look back on as significant. Today you will be taking action that will allow you to become younger and to live longer and more healthily.

Diet and Ageing

To lengthen thy life lessen thy meals.
BENJAMIN FRANKLIN

We are what we eat, and this is especially true with ageing. If you want to look and feel fabulous throughout your life, you need to pay attention to what you eat, and this becomes more important as you get older since every single atom in your body is fuelled by food.

There are many good books extolling the benefits of a healthy diet. In this book I will show you what I call nature's superfoods or wonderfoods, foods that if included in your diet will give you the vitamins, the super-nutrition and the anti-oxidants that will allow you to successfully fight ageing.

Anti-oxidants are nutrients, vitamins C and E and beta-carotene; they are found in fruits, vegetables, nuts and seeds. Anti-oxidants are the body's defence against free radicals and free radical damage. Free radicals are highly reactive molecules that surge through the body causing oxidization damage to all kinds of cells. They damage healthy genes and cells, and are linked to the onset of ageing as well as to cancer and heart disease. Anti-oxidants offer protection against free radicals. Foods that contain betacarotene and vitamins C and E are known as free radical scavengers.

For many people, adhering to a particular eating regime is difficult, especially if they have to prepare food for family members who don't share their enthusiasm for healthy eating or if their business involves a lot of entertaining or eating out. Many healthy eating plans fail because they are too rigid and inflexible so can be difficult to stick with, causing people to think: *I can't do this properly so I might as well not do it at all.*

I am going to show you all the foods that are truly nature's best, and I recommend that you include them in your diet. Those marked with an asterisk are the best of all. If you include as many of these foods as possible in your weekly eating plan, you will reap the benefits.

This will allow you to put together an eating plan that suits you, is easy to adhere to and adapts well to eating out and catering for others. You can easily use this eating plan while travelling and for packed lunches – in fact you can include it everywhere.

This list is not meant to replace your diet but to help you

ensure that you always include the best foods within it. You could exist very healthily on this diet alone, but you don't have to.

The more of these foods you include the healthier you will be. If you eat predominantly healthy food, your body can cope with you eating unhealthy food occasionally. Certainly making changes such as replacing butter and margarine with olive oil or superspread, and giving up hydrogenated oils, will help you to look and feel your best, because fat, especially hydrogenated fat, can accelerate oxygen-based damage to cells.

Cutting calories will have the same effect, but only if you eat food that is nourishing. We can live 50 per cent longer on a lean diet. Tests have been done on mice, rats, monkeys and squirrels, showing that if their calorie intake is reduced they live 50 per cent longer, have less oxygen-based damage to their cells, and delay the onset of disease. It is not a question of under-eating, but of eating food that is lean and healthy, eating much less fat and sugar and more fruits, vegetables and grains. Eating this way will cause you to consume fewer calories naturally, but you don't have to feel hungry or go hungry – the stress of that is not recommended or anti-ageing.

In alphabetical order, here is the list of wonderfoods that are essential to anti-ageing.

Apples are very rich in oxygen and the skins contain pectin, which is a setting agent and is very good for diarrhoea. Pectin, which is an anti-cholesterol agent, can lower cholesterol and can also reduce blood pressure. Pectin also helps rid the body of metals, which is vital if we are to fight ageing. Apples contain phytoestrogens, substances found in plants that may be able to prevent harmful oestrogens from causing breast cancer.

Apricots These are part of the staple diet of the Hunzas, who routinely seem to live into their hundredth year. Dried apricots are excellent too, but only if you buy them from health food shops and they aren't coated in preservatives. The black dried apricots from Turkey and the Hunza apricots are the best. Apricots contain lycopene and betacarotene, which protect against age-related cell damage and oxidation of proteins and fats, while boosting the immune system.

*Avocado This is one of the best foods of all. It is packed with vitamins, including vitamin E, minerals and anti-oxidants, and it has more potassium than bananas (potassium lowers blood pressure and reduces high sodium levels). Avocado is rich in glutathione, which protects the body from toxins, helps to neutralize the bad fat that damages our bodies, and is the most powerful anti-oxidant, fighting the free radical damage to cells which is a major cause of all ageing.

American studies have shown that people with the highest levels of glutathione had lower blood pressure, lower cholesterol and were generally leaner and healthier. Research studies showed that when mosquitoes deficient in glutathione were given the right amount their lifespan increased by 40 per cent.

Avocados are themselves high in fat, but it is a good fat that the body needs and makes excellent use of. Avocados have been proven to lower and improve blood cholesterol.

I find it best to use avocado in place of other fats – for instance, avocado spread on brown bread instead of butter and topped with tomatoes and red and yellow peppers makes a delicious sandwich which is healthy and not high in fat. I also spread it on rice cakes or crispbread, or mix it with salad, rice or pasta instead of a dressing.

Mashed-up avocado spread over the face, allowed to dry, and then washed off, makes an excellent face pack and is restoring for tired, stressed skin.

*Beetroot is wonderful for the endocrine system and is an anti-cancer food. Lightly cooked beetroot is wonderful in salads and sandwiches. Raw beetroot is excellent juiced into carrot or carrot and apple juice – about one part beetroot to three parts other juice.

Berries All the red, black and blue berries are crammed full of anti-oxidants and quercetin, which fight ageing. Strawberries are full of iodine and pectin and seem able to fight cancer in older people. Blueberries and cranberries are good for urinary tract infections, but don't add sugar to them as sugar feeds infection. As with all produce, buy organic berries if you can, or ensure that you wash them really well. Some cooks believe that washing strawberries spoils the flavour, but you must wash fruit or you will ingest all the pesticides and chemicals which damage cells and accelerate ageing.

Brazil Nuts Brazil nuts still in their shell are full of selenium, which is essential for anti-ageing. Each unshelled Brazil nut contains about 100 mcg of selenium more than most selenium tablets. Other food sources of selenium are grains, sunflower seeds, garlic and seafood. You don't need more than 200 mcg, and having two Brazil nuts daily or every other day will give you all the selenium you need. If you eat the other selenium-rich foods mentioned, then one Brazil nut daily or every other day would be enough. Brazil nuts out of their shell have much less selenium and can be rancid if they have been stored for too long.

*Broccoli This truly is a superfood. It deserves to be in the top ten of all foods, as it contains properties that fight bone loss and cancer. Broccoli contains sulphorophane, which boosts anti-cancer enzymes. 3.5 oz of broccoli contains 205 mg of calcium – more than any other vegetable. It is also rich in iron and folic acid.

Broccoli contains masses of anti-oxidants, including Vitamin C, betacarotene, glutathione (which neutralizes bad fats), quercetin and potassium. Broccoli also contains chromium and helps rid the body of the harmful type of oestrogen that can cause cancer, while quercetin protects against heart disease and heart attacks. Purple sprouting broccoli is even better, as it contains iron, calcium and folic acid. All types of broccoli boost the immune system.

*Cabbage Savoy cabbage is the best type, and is full of anti-oxidants. All cabbages have anti-cancer properties and are rich in potassium. Like broccoli, cabbage can help rid the body of the harmful oestrogens that can cause breast cancer. Red cabbage is also excellent. Cabbage contains indoles that help detoxify the body.

*Carrots lower blood cholesterol. The orange pigment in carrots boosts immune function and protects against cancer and strokes. The high levels of vitamin A in carrots are excellent for maintaining healthy skin, and the alphacarotene they contain may help prevent cardiovascular disease. Carrots really are good for your eyesight, as the betacarotene in carrots will protect you from eye-related diseases that often occur with ageing. Juicing is one of the best ways to eat carrots, and if you are serious about wanting to age slowly, a juicer can be one of your best investments.

Eggs These are a great source of sulphur, about 65 mg in each egg. They also contain zinc, iron, lecithin and trace minerals.

The athlete Stuart Mittleman swears by the properties of egg yolks, especially when training or competing. I consider myself very fortunate to have been able to learn from him how to run, and he has introduced me to the benefits of eggs and also of quinoa.

Make sure your eggs are organic and really fresh. Don't fry them in hot fat, but boil or poach them. Don't eat more than three eggs a week because they are high in cholesterol, particularly the yolks.

A beaten egg white applied to the face, allowed to dry, then washed off has a very tightening, lifting effect. Although the results are temporary and only last for about twenty-four hours, this has been used for centuries as a beauty treatment. It was used by the ancient Egyptians and was a favourite of film stars, as it made them look years younger.

*Fish Omega 3 oils are found in salmon, tuna, mackerel, sardines and herring, and to a lesser degree in halibut, cod and haddock. These same fish are also full of anti-oxidants, including selenium and co-enzyme Q 10.

Omega 3 oils are able to offer cells protection against ageing because they have blood-thinning properties that protect arteries and lower blood pressure. They also have anti-inflammatory properties and can protect against heart attacks, strokes and some cancers, while improving joint mobility.

The Omega 3 oils replace high amounts of Omega 6 fatty acids, which can be as bad as Omega 3 is good. Omega 6 is found in bad fats that damage our cells. Omega 3 oils have been proved to reverse a substantial amount of this damage. The vital ingredients in fish oil are EPA and DHA, which are essential fatty acids that the body needs and cannot make. You can only get these essential fatty acids by including fish or fish oil capsules in your diet (they are not in canned fish).

Japanese people, who live far longer than those in the West, eat 200 per cent more fish than we do. Seafood is high in magnesium. Bony fish, in particular salmon and sardines, are full of calcium. According to Danish research, Omega 3 fish oils may help pregnant mothers carry their babies to full term, and may be able to prolong gestation in mothers likely to give birth prematurely, because they shift the balance of production of prostaglandins involved in parturition.

*Garlic This helps to reduce fat. German studies show a garlic eater's increase in triglycerides after a meal to be 35 per cent lower than a non-garlic eater's. Garlic also helps maintain circulation to the skin, and this supply of oxygenated blood helps skin, hair and nails to stay strong, healthy and resilient. Garlic contains quercetin and 400 chemicals including many anti-oxidants. It is a natural antibiotic and decongestant and reduces cholesterol and blood pressure while boosting the immune system.

*Ginger This has an ability to deter blood clots, due to gingerol, an anti-coagulant and a blood thinner contained within ginger. It is similar to aspirin but much preferable, since it won't irritate your stomach. Ginger is excellent at reversing signs of hearing loss and arthritis; it also helps with nausea during travel and pregnancy, with stomach distention, and helps digestion. It has been used in China for over 2,000 years and is used in 50 per cent of all oriental prescriptions. You don't need to take much ginger at all – it can be obtained in capsule form but it is also a great ingredient to cook with, especially in stir-fried vegetables, chicken dishes and breads. I add a slice of fresh ginger to home-made carrot juice, and make ginger tea with ginger root and lemon juice, sometimes adding a stick of cinnamon and a touch of honey. It is very soothing if you have a sore throat, and tastes delicious.

Grains, Legumes, Beans, Pulses Sprouted grains, brown rice, millet, buckwheat, barley and lentils are all foods high in anti-oxidants and magnesium. They are also high in B and E vitamins and are an excellent source of protein. They contain saponins, which can slow the growth of tumours. They also contain selenium, potassium, calcium, iron and zinc. Brown rice is one of the most balanced and complete foods, and can absorb toxic waste from the lining of the intestines. Rice bran can reduce blood cholesterol. Barley has anti-viral and anti-cancer properties, and is high in anti-oxidants. Millet is rich in protein, iron, potassium, magnesium and minerals that protect against heart disease. Buckwheat, which is actually not a wheat, is full of protein and contains lysine and rutin, which make capillaries stronger and improve circulation, blood pressure and lower blood cholesterol.

*Grapes If you have a sweet tooth, small green grapes are one of the sweetest fruits around and do an excellent job of curtailing the craving for sweetness. You will find that once you are eating less sugar it tastes too sweet and begins to lose its appeal. I used to have a sweet tooth, and would never have believed this myself – but it is true. With chocolate and other refined sugars the more you get a taste the more you want. Switching to fruit is the best thing if you plan to age well. Most of the refined sugar available isn't a food, it is a chemical.

Red grapes are better for you because all the anti-oxidants in grapes (and they contain at least twenty) are in the skin, and the deeper the hue of the skin the more anti-oxidants there are. The anti-oxidants in grapes have an anti-clogging ability and do great work for our arteries; the skin of red grapes also contains a cholesterol-lowering ingredient.

Honey Organic cold pressed honey is a wonderfood and was used by Egyptians as a common remedy for a variety of ailments. Honey has antiseptic healing properties and has been used to treat wounds by the Greeks, Romans and Chinese, among others. It was even used during the First World War as an antiseptic – it seems to cause bacteria to disintegrate and has been proved to kill infectious organisms.

Because honey is a form of sugar, you need only take in small amounts of it. The fact that it is good for you is not a good reason to overdo your consumption of it. Honey put on wounds can have a very healing effect, and honey applied to the face is good as a face mask and good for removing old skin cells which dull the complexion.

Many tribes of people who live to 100 and more, yet remain youthful, have a diet rich in bee pollen and propolis. Propolis is the substance made by bees to seal the hive together, protecting it from the outside world and creating a totally sterile environment. Propolis produces the auto-immune system for the hive and is antibiotic, anti-viral and anti-fungal. Propolis is also loaded with amino acids, vitamins, minerals and bio-flavinoids, which are very involved in the healing process. You can take propolis as a supplement – it has been found to be effective for colds, flu, many viruses, arthritis and rheumatic problems. 'Cold pressed' on the label means that the product has not been heat-treated, which causes it to lose essential vitamins.

Linseeds are a good source of Omega 3 and vitamin E, especially for vegans. They can be purchased as seeds and also as linseed oil. They are known as flax seeds/flaxseed oil in America and linseeds/linseed oil in England. This oil has been associated with a long, healthy life for years, and was used as a therapeutic remedy in Ancient Greece and Rome.

The essential fatty acids (EFAs) in linseed oil are used by the body for cell oxygenation and promote a healthy immune system. The body cannot produce EFAs so they must be supplied by food. Linseed oil has a natural detoxifying effect on the body and is known traditionally as a super skin nutrition to prevent drying and flaking skin.

If you take it in oil form, a few spoons a day is fine. Put it in salad dressings or on toast, but don't cook with it or you will destroy its benefits. Linseeds are also easy to take sprinkled on to food – because they don't have much of a flavour they can be added to yoghurt, cereals, soups, salads, breads and any cooked dishes. It is preferable to add them after cooking. They can also be added to juices.

Linseeds have a very well-deserved reputation as being an excellent, safe and natural remedy for constipation and its negative effects on the skin, and will draw toxins out of your body. If you are taking the seeds you must crack them with your teeth to release the oil or they will pass through your system intact. You can buy seeds already cracked called Linusit Gold in health food shops and chemists.

Liquorice Liquorice root is used in 50 per cent of all oriental and herbal medicines and prescriptions because it contains glycyrrhizin and triterpenoids, which enhance immune functions, fight gum disease, gingivitis and tooth decay, and can improve the liver function. It also has anti-tumour properties, guards against excessive oestrogens, and has proved very effective in the treatment of arthritis. Liquorice is a root that is fifty times sweeter than sugar cane yet has no calories. You can make the root into a delicious tea or buy liquorice tea in most health food shops. Confectionery liquorice has no benefits.

Oats have been shown to reduce blood pressure and to reduce cholesterol levels by 3 per cent (or 7 per cent if your cholesterol level is already high). Just 2 oz of oatbran daily can lower low-density lipoprotein (LDL) cholesterol by 15 per cent, so oats are a superfood if you want to protect your arteries. Oats also contain phytoestrogen, which can prevent the harmful type of oestrogen from leading to breast cancer.

Oatmeal rubbed on to the face or body and gently removed is a gentle, natural and cheap exfoliant that is far better for you than some of the cosmetic ones, which can contain harsh, unnatural ingredients.

Olive Oil Good for the heart. People who regularly eat olive oil have less cancer, especially breast cancer, less heart disease, and lower levels of cholesterol. Olive oil is high in quercetin. It is a good fat that can reverse some of the oxidation damage caused by trans fats. (See the section on foods to avoid.)

*Onions From the garlic family, these have been used for centuries to ward off colds and other ailments. They are a recognized anti-cancer food because they are rich in quercetin, an anti-oxidant that inhibits cancer-causing agents. It is also anti-inflammatory, anti-bacterial, anti-fungal and anti-viral. Onions are also full of digestive enzymes. They have been proved to prevent cancer, stomach cancer in particular, and to cleanse and thin the blood, protecting against blood clotting because of the quercetin. Onions are also full of allicin and glutathione, and they detoxify and boost the immune system. In Ireland onions have been used for years to dissolve blood clots in horses. Red onions are by far the best, followed by yellow onions. White onions don't have the same healing compounds or quercetin in them.

*Parsley Full of vitamins C and A, with some B vitamins, as well as zinc, iron, calcium and potassium, parsley is a natural diuretic and a great inner cleanser. It is great in juices and can be sprinkled on top rather than put through the juicer.

Parsley is regarded in some circles and by some nutritionists as the third most powerful food on earth. It is full of phytochemicals and helps maintain blood sugar levels.

Peppers Red and yellow peppers are the best, being highest in vitamin C. Peppers are high in glutathione, which is good for vision and neutralizes bad fats. Glutathione is found only in fresh green, red and yellow vegetables. Red peppers have more vitamin C than oranges.

*Quinoa is a grain used by the South American Incas. Nutritionally it is considered a superfood, as it contains all eight essential amino acids and is very rich in calcium and iron – so it is a good replacement for meat or dairy produce. It is rather like rice but cooks in half the time, and it seems to be a true energy-sustaining food – it is used by a lot of top athletes. It is great in soups, salads or casseroles.

Raisins are dried grapes, and can be just as effective as fresh ones as long as they aren't eaten with chemical residue on them.

*Seeds These include sunflower seeds, pumpkin seeds, sesame seeds and sprouted seeds. Pumpkin and squash seeds are full of zinc, vitamins and minerals; sunflower seeds are high in vitamin E and B vitamins. All seeds are high in magnesium and have some Omega 3 oils – they are a good source of protein.

*Soya products, which include soya flour, soya milk, soya yoghurt, soya beans and soya protein, often known as tofu (not soyabean oil or soy sauce), are all full of calcium and build strong bones. They protect us from osteoporosis, because soya products conserve calcium. Soya products contain phytoestrogen, which may be able to prevent oestrogen from causing breast cancer. Too much oestrogen stimulates cell growth; soya helps to minimize this naturally. Soya beans also offer protection against several other cancers because they contain genestien and daidzien, which are particularly strong anti-oxidants with anti-ageing and anti-cancer properties that also protect arteries and protect against blood clots, strokes and thrombosis, while lowering blood cholesterol and insulin levels. Soya also contains glycine and arginine, which lower insulin and keep blood sugar even, thus protecting against diabetes and weight gain. Some American researchers have called soya a universal cancer-preventative agent and an anti-cancer food.

Soya beans and the above foods made from soya beans can prevent some free radical damage and slow down ageing. Again, Japanese people, who live longer than any other race, also eat more soya beans. Soya beans are positively loaded with anti-oxidants and are a true superfood that deserves to be in the top three of the top ten wonderfoods. Most people in the West eat very little, but if you want to have young, healthy cells, eat some form of soya products daily. The Italian health service prescribe soya protein to reduce high levels of cholesterol.

The easiest way to eat soya is to use soya milk in place of dairy milk on cereals. Even better is to make milk shakes from fruit and soya milk by blending fresh or frozen berries or bananas, or any fruit you choose, with soya milk. Use soya yoghurt in place of dairy yoghurt, and in baking you can replace 10 per cent of any flour with soya flour. Tofu takes on the flavour of whatever you are cooking and is excellent in stir-fries, while soya beans are excellent in salads, soups and casseroles. Buy soya protein that does not have added salt.

*__Spinach__ Full of anti-oxidants, spinach is able to deter strokes, cancer, heart disease and high blood pressure, among other things. It deserves to be in the top ten of superfoods because it contains lutein, which is claimed to be an especially strong anti-ageing compound, and folic acid, which offers protection to the brain and arteries and is another anti-cancer agent. It also contains iron, calcium, potassium, and more protein than any other vegetable. Like carrots, spinach is excellent at protecting eyesight. It is also high in magnesium.

Thyme Thyme is a herb rather than a food, but I have included it because it has more anti-ageing compounds than any other herb. It is therefore well worth adding thyme to your diet by including it in cooked dishes, salads and soups or making a herb tea from it.

*Tomatoes contain quercetin and the excellent anti-oxidant lycopene, which has proved to be a super-efficient free radical scavenger and preserves mental and physical functions in the very old. Lycopene can also protect against cancer of the cervix, digestive tract, stomach, colon, prostate, lung and pancreas. Eating ten servings of tomatoes a week, can reduce the risk of prostate cancer in men by 35 per cent. Lycopene protects against age-related cell damage and oxidation to proteins and fats. It is saved during heating, so you can safely take your intake of tomatoes raw, juiced and in sauces and cooked dishes.

Wheat Germ is full of B vitamins while wheat germ oil contains Omega 3 oils and is a separate and different food from wheat, which is usually very adulterated. Buy organic wheat germ.

*Yams contain natural progesterone and other hormones. In certain tribes, when women are going through the menopause, they eat lots of yams and don't seem to suffer with hot flushes or depression. It is very useful to eat or juice yams at this time. Japanese women also seem to have little trouble with the menopause, and this has been linked to their diet being rich in soya and Omega 3 fish oil.

Yoghurt Only live natural yoghurt is a superfood – this is because of the acidophilus which encourages friendly beneficial flora in the intestines. Always buy natural yoghurt with live active cultures; they help fight yeast infections and aid digestion and boost the immune system.

Add to this list all orange and yellow fruits such as peaches, mangoes, papayas, pineapples, lemons, oranges, grapefruits, and orange and yellow vegetables such as sweet potatoes, squash, pumpkins, swedes and turnips. Add also all deeply coloured fruits and vegetables such as watermelons (contain lycopene), melons, aubergines and radichio.

The more dark green or richly red or yellow and orange the colour, the richer the anti-oxidant content within.

Green leafy vegetables are also a good source of calcium and a good alternative to dairy produce. They help detoxify the body and boost the immune system.

Eating a high-protein, high-meat diet can cause the uric acid that these foods contain to wash calcium out of the bones, and can mean just as much of a threat of osteoporosis as being calcium-deficient.

The National Cancer Institute label oranges a total package of every anti-cancer inhibitor in existence. Grapefruits contain compounds that lower blood cholesterol and may reverse atherosclerosis, which is the largest killer of women over 60 in the West, because all citrus fruits contain limones which increase the manufacture of enzymes involved in detoxifying the body and also lower cholesterol and reduce plaque in the arteries. Grapefruits are an excellent source of glutathione. Make sure you eat the pith as well, since many of the grapefruit's benefits are stored there.

If you eat plenty of fruits, vegetables and grains, and include the listed superfoods in your diet, you will be getting plenty of fibre, which is essential in any diet. Fibre can help fight heart disease, cancer, high cholesterol and blood pressure and atherosclerosis.

Fibre is an indigestible substance that makes up a plant's structure. It passes through our digestive system without being broken down or digested, and takes cholesterol, bile acids and toxins out of our body during its journey.

Most people are only aware of the importance of fibre in alleviating constipation, yet it does much more than that. Cholesterol can build up in the blood and will lead to clogged arteries if it is not removed and passed out of the body as bile acids from the digestive tract.

Foods to avoid if you want to age well are:

Smoked foods, cured meats, bacon, sausages and hot dogs, as they are very carcinogenic and full of nitrates.

Barbecued foods, because the smoke and heat of the barbecues produce many cancer-causing compounds, particularly *nitrosamine*, the most powerful of all carcinogens. Don't barbecue frequently (which isn't too much of a hardship in Britain), ensure the grill is high above the coals, and wrap the food and even the grill pan in foil to stop fat dripping on to the coals and causing even more smoke and heat.

Definitely avoid hydrogenated fats, especially margarines and foods cooked in fat that may be rancid such as crisps, popcorn, pre-packaged foods, etc., because hydrogenated oils increase the amount of free radicals in the body and cause a lot of damage to cells. By far the worst fats to eat are the polyunsaturated kind such as corn oil and safflower oil and those containing cholesterol, which can only come from foods of animal origin. Trans fats, which are made by solidifying hydrogenated fats into margarine and shortening, need to be avoided because they cause so much cellular damage. They are found in cakes, biscuits, crisps and processed foods. One of the reasons Mediterranean countries have a lower incidence of heart disease is that they consume less bad fat and more good fat, and eat foods very high in quercetin, glutathione and lycopene.

Safe and healthy fats are the monounsaturate ones, such as olive oil, fish oil, linseed oil, avocado, olive, and almond oil. Ensure you eat all the foods from the list that contain glutathione, because this helps to defuse free radical activity from fats and are able to neutralize rancid fat.

A high-fat diet is very much linked to accelerated ageing. Studies by scientist Dr Richard Hochschild have shown that ten servings a day of high-fat food will age an average 45-year-old by six years, whereas just replacing red meat with fish and chicken can leave you biologically four years younger.

A high-fat diet can also encourage tumours. Your diet needs to be only 15 per cent fat and 15–18 per cent protein.

Avoid foods high in sugar, because sugar rots the digestive system. Avoid heavily processed foods and foods full of preservatives and excessive salt. Too much salt reduces calcium absorption.

Aloe Vera is another wonderfood – it is taken as a juice and has been shown to have very beneficial effects on irritable bowel syndrome, fatigue, skin complaints, arthritis, ulcers and a host of other ailments as well as being an energy booster. Aloe has been proven to ease and improve the digestion and absorption of food and improve bowel function. It is more of a specialist type of drink than a food, and can be purchased in most health food shops. Make sure the type you buy has the seal of approval from the International Aloe Science Council.

Aloe Vera works by increasing cellular growth and enzyme activity and by accelerating tissue regeneration. It replaces dead tissue with healthy tissue while increasing the body's resistance to infection and disease. It is also a wonderful soothing moisturizer, a skin food, and excellent for sunburn.

Water is not so much a wonderfood but an absolutely essential part of feeling and looking well, of enjoying excellent health, and of living at all. Water is needed by every cell and tissue in the body. It is essential for digestion and circulation and does everything from carrying nutrients throughout the body to taking waste and toxins out of the body. Our cells cannot regenerate or repair themselves properly without water.

Even with weight loss, you need to drink enough water to be able to lose weight properly. If you don't drink enough water you won't be able to flush toxins out of your system and your body may send out signals you interpret as hunger, causing you to over-eat when what the body really wants and needs is water. The body needs a constant supply of water as we lose so much every day through sweat, urine and even through our breath. When we become dehydrated we get weak, tired and misinterpret body signals.

In order to look and feel younger you must drink eight large glasses or 2 litres of water daily, you need to drink it throughout the day, because if you try to take in a huge amount of water all at once your body will pass it out of your system again too quickly.

Because your body needs a constant supply of water, it is best to get into the habit of drinking a large glass on rising, then seven more throughout the day and even more if you are losing body fluids through exercise, perspiration or flu or diarrhoea. Drinking enough water will be an asset to your skin and to your energy levels. Drinking tea, coffee, alcohol and colas does not rehydrate your body, since these liquids have a diuretic effect on the body. Far from giving you fluid, they have a depleting, dehydrating effect. For every tea, coffee or cola type of beverage you drink you will need to drink an additional glass of water. Don't wait until you feel thirsty to drink, as by then your body is already dehydrated.

Our bodies are made of 90 per cent water, our bones, blood, cells, muscles and organs are all mostly composed of water. As we age we lose more and more water from our bodies, causing our faces to look shrunken and our skin to look wrinkled.

Quote
Every man desires to live long but no man would be old.

JONATHAN SWIFT

Vitamins, Supplements and Ageing

Taking the right amount of vitamins and supplements has a very important part to play in looking, feeling and becoming years younger. Dr Linus Pauling, the renowned American scientist and winner of the Nobel Prize, believed we could all add sixteen to twenty-four years to our lives by eating a healthy, balanced diet. He also believed that optimum nutrition was the medicine of the future.

While it is true that the vitamins found in fruits and vegetables can be better than vitamins taken in tablet form, we can no longer truly tell the vitamin content of the foods we buy and eat. The quality of the food we eat is linked directly to the quality of the soil it is grown in, and unfortunately much of our food is grown in soil that is very poor in minerals and selenium. Also, much of our seemingly fresh food is irradiated and treated with pesticides and other agents that can counteract their vitamin benefits. A lot of the food we buy as fresh can be days, sometimes weeks old, and its vitamin content will have been reduced by storage.

Organic produce is better because it is grown without pesticides and chemicals, but even some organic produce is grown in soil that is very poor and again lacking in selenium. Apart from growing your own food and regularly replenishing the soil, the only way you can be certain you are getting the vitamins essential for successful ageing is to take them in supplement form.

A survey conducted by the Ministry of Agriculture, Fisheries and Food reported that only one in ten British people get even the basic recommended daily allowance of nutrients from food. Medical researcher Dr Stephen Davies tested the blood levels of vitamin B in thousands of people and found that seven out of ten were deficient

Taking the RDA (Recommended Daily Allowance) does not make allowances for people who smoke, drink, are recovering from illness or infection, are on the pill, live in a polluted city, or are stressed or elderly, since the RDA is the recommended daily allowance for a person who is assumed to be already healthy.

Furthermore, if you have any problems with digestion and absorption you may be passing vital elements straight out of your system, as you will see in the next section on digestion and ageing. A blood test can show you the level of vitamins in your blood, so you know how effective your absorption is, and will show up any deficiencies you need to attend to.

Cooking can destroy most vitamins in food, even the allicin in garlic, which is a natural antibiotic. Even if you had the time and the tenacity to prepare fresh, organic, raw food daily, you would have to eat masses of it to ensure that your vitamin intake was sufficient to reverse ageing – obviously this can be done but it is time-consuming, does not adapt well to eating out or accommodating the needs of family eating, and some people don't digest raw food as well as food that is lightly cooked.

With some vitamins, such as vitamin E, which is found in vegetable oils, fish oils, raw nuts, seeds and beans, you would need to take in a lot of oil and far too many calories in order to get the amount of vitamins necessary. Although the above foods are very healthy and absolutely good for you, it has also been proved that another way to live longer while looking younger is to eat less, to take in fewer calories – this has always extended lifespan in animals (and in the humans who have will-ingly chosen this way of eating). Cutting calories also limits free radical damage.

If you think you are getting an abundance of vitamins in fruit juices, think again. If the juice you buy says 'made from con-centrate' on the carton, then all the vitamins have been boiled and heat-treated out of it. It is better to buy juices that are 'freshly pressed', but even then the quality of the juice within is only as good as the quality and freshness of the produce it was made with. It is much better to juice your own fruits and vegetables using organic produce.

With vitamins it is essential to take the right amount and to take all the vitamins that you need. If you miss out on some of the vitamin family it can cause those you *are* taking to work less effectively or not work at all. Anti-oxidants work together – they are not so effective on their own, but combined with other anti-oxidants and essential nutrients they are highly effective in detoxifying your system, fighting free radicals and slowing down age degeneration. They boost the immune system and can be used in natural healing and in the prevention and treatment of cancers and heart disease.

In his lectures and books, Dr Richard Passwater documents the role vitamin supplements have to play in preventing and fighting cancer. He has been researching the role of nutrients in slowing down ageing for thirty-seven years, and is one of the best authorities on the subject. His latest book is *The New Super Nutrition*.

Vitamin supplements can strengthen the immune system and destroy newly formed cancer cells before they multiply. This is especially true of the vitamins A, C, E, selenium and betacarotene.

While taking vitamins correctly can absolutely cause you to look and feel younger and you will definitely benefit from this, it is important to remember that a lot of the effects are cumulative and retroactive, and that some of the vitamins are preventing signs of illness and ageing that you may not notice for twenty years.

Vitamins are not meant to replace a healthy diet or to allow you to live on junk food and still get the vitamins you need. Within this programme of becoming and remaining ten years younger, I highly recommend that you eat the wonderfoods and take vitamins and supplements so that your body has at its disposal every tool you need to fight ageing successfully.

Below is a list of recommended vitamins, along with the particular property of each vitamin or supplement. Although they are listed individually they do not need to be taken individually – many can be taken in multivitamin form along with additional C and E, for example.

Vitamin A Helps maintain young, smooth, soft skin, reduces susceptibility to infection and can protect the lungs from pollution damage. It is essential for the maintenance of healthy skin, eyes, bones, hair and teeth. Take 10,000 IU (international units) daily; 10,000 IU sounds a lot, but you could safely take 20,000.

Vitamin B1 Helps to stimulate the immune system and is a natural anti-oxidant. It is also good for the digestion and the nervous system.

Vitamin B2 Helps to prevent cataracts and to produce anti-bodies to fight infection. It is necessary for healthy skin and eyes and helps to release energy from foods.

Vitamin B3 I recommend this to all my patients who are giving up smoking, because of its wonderful ability to promote blood flow and dilate blood vessels damaged by smoking abuse – this brings vital nutrients to the skin and helps cells detoxify. It is also excellent for digestion and for the nervous system and is essential for maintenance of healthy skin and for proper mental functioning.

Vitamin B6 Helps to prevent arteriosclerosis (hardening of the arteries) and heart disease.

Vitamin B12 Helps to prevent anaemia and to maintain healthy red blood cells and a healthy nervous system. Boosts energy and can counteract depression. Take 500 mcg.

Vitamin C Essential in the manufacture of collagen, it helps to keep muscles firm and prevents skin from bagging, sagging and wrinkling as well as maintaining teeth, gums, bones and blood vessels. Vitamin C has been shown to reverse ageing by six years, and is a superior free radical scavenger and anti-oxidant. It helps to form red blood cells and can prevent internal bleeding and those hated and ageing broken veins. Vitamin C is also a natural healer used in many cancer therapies. You can safely take up to 17 grams a day, and some people take even more. A good guide is to take at least 1 gram (1,000 mg) and up to 5 grams a day to maintain health, and between 5 and 10 grams to slow down ageing. You can even increase the dose, since vitamin C is not stored in the body. You may find excess vitamin C has a laxative effect initially, so adjust the dose accordingly.

Vitamin D This can slow down ageing while improving life-span and quality of life. It can also help with psoriasis. Vitamin D is needed to help our bones absorb calcium. Without it they absorb only 10 per cent of your calcium intake, with it they absorb 80–90 per cent of your calcium intake. Take 200 IU daily.

Vitamin E This has healing properties when applied to minor cuts, burns and abrasions. It is also super-nutrition for the skin and revitalizing for tired, stressed skin. Use pure, natural vitamin E in capsule form as a supplement to skin cream. I have used it on cuts to prevent scarring with great success, and used it during my pregnancy to prevent stretch marks. Free radicals are absorbed by vitamin E. It is effective in preventing and treating many diseases, including some cancers and heart disease, as well as offering resistance to many others, boosting the immune system, and repairing red blood cells. A study in the *New England Journal of Medicine*, using over 87,000 women, found that women who took vitamin E supplements for over two years had a 40 per cent lower risk of heart disease. It has also been proved to reduce sun damage to skin.

Russian scientists using vitamin E on ageing patients found

that it increased stamina and strength, and improved sleep patterns along with a disappearance of wrinkles and even of grey hair.

You can safely take between 400 and 1,000 IU daily.

Selenium This has anti-cancer properties, offers protection from some types of cancer and heart problems, and naturally detoxifies the body of metals. Selenium greatly improves immune function, has been shown to reverse ageing and has been proved to reduce sun damage to the skin.

The average daily intake of selenium is only 43 mcg. The World Health Organization recommends between 50 and 200 mcg as safe and adequate. Children can quite safely take selenium – start them on 10 mcg and build up to 50 mcg. Adults can safely take 300–400 mcg daily.

Calcium Vital for healthy teeth and bones and good for digestion. If you take a combined calcium/magnesium supplement it can stop you craving sugar. If you are low in magnesium you often have high blood pressure, can be prone to migraines and may crave sugar. Always take calcium supplements with meals, as the stomach acid produced while eating also breaks down calcium carbonate and helps its absorption. Take 500–1,500 mg daily.

Betacarotene Offers great anti-ageing properties, protects body cells and tissues, and is excellent in protecting skin, lungs and the immune system. Betacarotene can also protect against and treat the damaging effects of the sun's UV rays. Take 2,500 IU or 6–30 mg daily.

Chromium Has been shown to extend the lifespan of animals by 33 per cent. Take 100 mg daily.

Echinacea This is a wonderful booster for the immune system – I have never had a cold since I began to take it. I discovered echinacea in America. You can also buy echinacea combined with cat's claw and goldenseal, which is wonderful for the immune system, the skin and the digestion.

Spirulina This is a natural anti-oxidant and can improve skin texture. It is a form of freshwater-growing algae (algae are one of the things in nature than never grow old), and contains concentrated amounts of all the nutrients found in green vegetables. It was used in Minsk on all the children suffering from radiation after Chernobyl, because spirulina was able to help detoxify their bodies.

Buy only the best kind of spirulina, which has been grown under controlled conditions. Doses will vary according to whether you buy it in powder or tablet form. You will need about 16 tablets or 3 large spoonfuls daily.

Co-enzyme 10 An excellent anti-oxidant that boosts immune function and has a protective effect on the heart and on cell membranes. It also converts energy from food to our cells and is recommended if you have poor digestion or absorption. Take 30 mg daily.

Ginkgo Biloba A powerful anti-oxidant which seems to have an anti-ageing effect on the brain, this can reverse declining memory and is excellent at improving blood circulation, especially to the brain. Ginkgo biloba carries oxygen and blood to diseased areas of the body and is known as a 'smart drug' because of its ability to improve and restore memory, concentration and circulation. Ginkgo biloba also contains bioflavonoids. Take 80 mg daily.

Zinc This fights free radicals, as it is another excellent anti-oxidant. It is also good for improving memory and vision, maintaining fertility and libido and loss of taste or smell. Take 20–25 mg daily.

GLA Gamma linolenic acid balances hormone function and is known to help with PMS and the menopause. It also helps keep joints supple and has a natural and proven anti-inflammatory effect. GLA is one of the essential fatty acids needed by our bodies to maintain the structure of cell membranes. In the body it is converted to a substance which regulates every cell and organ of the body and controls the activities of key enzymes. GLA has been shown to help dyslexic and hyperactive children, because a lack of essential fatty acids is indicated as a trigger to behaviour problems. It also protects against the effects of smoking and pollution and improves skin. GLA is also contained within evening primrose oil. Buy only natural evening primrose oil. Take 2,000 mg.

Sulphur Like chromium, sulphur has been shown to extend the lifespan of animals. It also protects us from too much exposure to electricity.

Japanese Green Tea A powerful anti-oxidant and metabolism booster, this anti-oxidant-rich tea contains chemicals called methylxanthines, which seem to boost metabolism and burn fat more rapidly. It also reduces cholesterol. It can be bought in leaf, teabag or even capsule form in most health food shops.

Kombucha Fungus Tea This is something fairly new to Britain, and has many fans. It has been around in Russia and China for 2,000 years, and is packed with anti-oxidants, rich in anti-bacterial acids and B complex vitamins, boosts the immune system, and is an excellent detoxifier. It is said to help with arthritis, cancer and MS, and to have amazing healing and anti-ageing properties. It is claimed that it has eliminated wrinkles and grey hair. Because it is a living organism you need to brew your own from an original fungus, which you can get from Kombucha Network, PO Box 1887, Bath BA2 8YA. It tastes a little like cider and is definitely an acquired taste.

Since you only need to pay a nominal sum of a few pounds

for the first fungus, it is a source of almost cost-free anti-oxidants. This is very useful for those on a limited budget, because it can be very expensive buying all the vitamins necessary to defy ageing.

I cannot tell you exactly which vitamins from the above list to take, because what you need to take is linked to your age and state of health. Since the amount and type of vitamins you take is personal and relates to your own health, age and dietary needs, I can only recommend that you take a very good brand of multivitamin/mineral along with extra C and E, selenium, spirulina and echinacea. You could add to this Co-enzyme 10, calcium and ginkgo biloba, especially if you are over 50, plus any other supplement listed above that relates to your particular situation.

Digestion and Ageing

Good digestion is linked to ageing well, whereas poor digestion can accelerate the ageing process and disrupt every system in the body, including cell regeneration. If you have digestion problems, food is not absorbed properly into the blood or assimilated into cells and tissues, leaving you nutritionally deficient regardless of how good your diet is.

Digestion is essential to good health and essential to looking and remaining young. Without digestion the body could not survive. If our digestion is less than 100 per cent, it follows that we are also less than 100 per cent. If you have inadequate digestion, then taking all the foods and vitamins listed previously won't have a positive effect on you because they will not be fully absorbed. Some people have digestion that is so bad they don't even absorb 10 per cent of the vitamins or nutrients in their diet.

Digestion is a complex process, using acids, alkalis and enzymes. It uses up huge amounts of energy, which is why when we over-eat we tend to feel sleepy or fall asleep. This is because the brain diverts oxygen and blood away from major organs in order to use it in digestion.

Many people have digestion problems – disorders of the stomach, intestines, gall bladder, liver and pancreas can all lead to poor digestion, as does existing or having existed on a diet of over-processed and over-refined food. Eating food full of preservatives means that the same preservative that stopped bacteria growing on your potato or piece of bread will also stop your digestive system from being able to work fully. When faced with preservatives the body has to make more and more digestive juices in order to break down food, and when it becomes so overworked it eventually works less efficiently. This is another reason for buying more organic produce.

Tension can disrupt digestion, because eating when tense, tired, emotional or overwrought will interfere with the free flow of digestive enzymes, leaving the eater with indigestion and very little or no energy released from the food.

Just a look at the sales figures for indigestion pills and antacids is proof of the enormous number of people with digestion problems – in England over 45 million are sold yearly; however, many people don't understand the long-term effects poor digestion has on general health and on ageing. If you are suffering from poor digestion, wonderful help is at hand in the form of digestive enzymes, which help to digest food when your own digestive system fails to complete the process.

There are many enzymes involved in digestion, including pepsin, trypsin, rennin and pancreatin, and it is best to buy a digestive enzyme that contains all of these. By taking digestive enzymes you are helping your body absorb food and get all the vitamins it needs, and you are maintaining better energy, since when you don't digest food properly your body is forced to suck blood from your brain and muscles in an attempt to redigest food, leaving you feeling sleepy and lacking energy.

When we don't digest food correctly it tends to sit in the stomach while the body makes more attempts at digestion. Eventually the food will ferment and putrefy, producing toxic elements which cause the skin to break out and look sallow, along with a host of other unpleasant effects which include premature ageing, allergies, headaches, lethargy, depression and protruding veins. These all result from our body being forced to reabsorb poisons.

Taking digestive enzymes can eliminate all these symptoms. If your digestion is poor, I recommend that you take them with every meal. If you only have poor digestion when you over-eat or eat certain types of food, then take them then, and always keep some digestive enzymes in your purse or wallet – they are miracle workers. I don't take them all the time, but I always have some to hand, and usually find myself giving them away to people who might benefit from them – and they always do.

Studies have shown that up to 40 per cent of the elderly may have hypochlorhydria, a condition in which the stomach is not acid enough, leading to mineral deficiencies from poor digestion which can in turn lead to osteoporosis and fragile bones. Taking calcium supplements won't always help, because people with hypochlorhydria can't absorb calcium or magnesium carbonate.

I had poor digestion for years before I understood its far-reaching effects. Like many people, I was concerned only with treating the symptoms rather than tackling the cause.

It is quite easy to establish whether or not you have digestion problems by answering a few simple questions.

After eating

Do you feel bloated or swollen, do you need to loosen clothing, or does clothing feel uncomfortably tight for long periods?

Do you get a lot of gas?

Do you feel nausea or have stomach pain?

Do you feel tired, sleepy, lethargic?

Do you get headaches after eating?

Do you sometimes get diarrhoea after eating? Or constipation?

If you are experiencing any of these symptoms, then you have poor digestion or malabsorption, which means you aren't absorbing or benefiting from the nutrients in your food. It also means your body is working too hard at digestion. When this happens frequently, the body is forced to leach enzymes out of other organs such as the pancreas to use for digestion.

The enzymes used in digestion are also used in cell renewal, and have a vital part to play in preventing disease and age degeneration. We must have a sufficient supply of pancreatic enzymes in order for cells to work properly, and in order to sustain immunity to many diseases such as cancer. When enzymes are continually being removed from the pancreas for digestion it has a dreadful effect on ageing.

The same thing happens if you always eat very late at night then go to bed. First, you won't enjoy proper sleep because your body is busy digesting food instead of resting. Second, your body takes enzymes from the pancreas to digest the food when these enzymes are already earmarked to be used in the process of cellular repair, and renewal and rebuilding of the body, which always takes place at night, and also to fight any developing cancer. If your body is digesting, the whole process of cell repair and regeneration is set aside, and although this is acceptable occasionally it has a terrible effect on your health and looks if it happens too frequently.

I'm not a killjoy – I wouldn't dream of suggesting you cease going out to dinner or having late-night dinner parties, especially since this is something I enjoy myself.

Here are the changes you can make that will allow you to enjoy yourself while maintaining optimum health and looking young:

1. Don't regularly eat very late at night. If you like to eat something late, eat fruit, since it is raw and easily and quickly digested. Also your metabolic rate is at its lowest in the evening, so if you starve all day and eat late at night you will find it much harder to lose weight.

2. Always take digestive enzymes when you do eat at night, since they will do the job of breaking down and digesting the food for you, leaving your pancreas free to do its perfect work repairing cells.
3. Eat less cooked food at night, more raw. Include foods like pineapple and papaya, which are full of natural digestive enzymes. Cooked food tends to be food without enzymes; raw foods of plant and vegetable origin retain enzymes when eaten and thus don't need to take enzymes from the body for use in digestion.
4. Don't eat when you are feeling very stressed or very tired or emotional, because tension will limit the free flow of digestive enzymes. If you feel you have to eat and you are feeling very tense or tired, take digestive enzymes.
5. Don't eat too quickly. Slow down and chew your food, since much digestion begins in the mouth. Don't eat too much.
6. Don't eat too many varieties of food. Keep your food quite simple, and don't have too many different dishes or types of food, since this is much harder for the body to digest. Don't have very rich or spicy food, because the more simple and basic your food is the easier it is to digest.
7. Heavy meats and oily, fatty foods are very hard to digest. A good rule of the thumb is that the body is designed to digest food that grows in the earth and in the trees, natural foods that are lightly cooked. Cheese and milk don't come into this category, because they are so concentrated and were never designed for human consumption – don't eat a lot of dairy produce.

Ice cream and cheese are notoriously hard to digest. It is said that some 80 per cent of the world's population cannot digest milk protein properly – this is known as lactose intolerance or an inability to digest dairy produce. Children under 10 are more easily able to digest milk products because they have an enzyme in their bodies called lactase, which is specifically there to digest lactose. Without lactase, an enzyme that declines in humans from the age of 10, most dairy produce will go through the digestive system undigested.

To make matters worse, dairy produce contains casein, which is an insoluble protein that plugs up the intestinal tract. Cooked cheese especially sticks to the walls of the intestines like glue. Yoghurt is easier to digest because of the healthy bacteria in it – the live active cultures in real yoghurt break down lactose in the intestines, so natural live yoghurt is an exception to the rule on dairy produce and is a good food for the body. Fruit-flavoured, sugared yoghurts, frozen yoghurt and yoghurt-covered raisins don't count; the latter are just fat- and sugar-covered raisins with milk powder added.

Wheat is another product that many people have problems digesting, because it is so over-processed and is usually grown with an abundance of chemicals and pesticides. Organic wheat and wheat products avoid this. Also people eat it too often, for breakfast, lunch and dinner, in the form of bread, cereals, cakes, biscuits, pies, sandwiches, pizza, pasta, noodles, crackers, snack-bars and a variety of other foods, building up an intolerance to it. White flour mixed with water makes great glue. The gluten in flour and in flour products, when eaten as part of a food like bread, becomes a glue-like substance that sticks to the intestine wall and sticks to other foods passing through the intestine. It does not pass out of the body very easily and can remain in the intestines for years.

Even if you feel your digestion is good, it is still worth taking digestive enzymes every time you have a heavy meal, a late meal or a meal that is greatly varied or based on over-processed food. Many people who are serious about wanting to look younger and feel great take digestive enzymes daily as a matter of course. Bread is so convenient – use rye or oat bread instead.

If you seem to be intolerant to some foods but can't resist the occasional pizza or ice cream, take digestive enzymes to minimize the damage – but don't use them as an excuse to eat a terrible diet. Even if you take digestive enzymes with every meal, you still need to pay attention to your diet and eat more natural, healthy and preferably organic food and less processed, refined and junk food.

The best kinds of digestive enzymes are vegetable-based – papaya for example. Chlorella, from the spirulina family, is a natural digestive enzyme. You can buy digestive enzymes in any health food shop.

Electricity and Ageing

The effect of electricity on our bodies is something that has only recently come to light, since only a few generations ago people had very little electricity in their homes – just the lights and a radio. Even in the last fifteen years our use of personal electric items has massively increased, with the advent of mobile phones, laptop computers, pagers, personal organizers and so on.

When I bought my first home, about fifteen years ago, it was a new conversion but it had only two socket points in the bed-room and three in the lounge. This was normal, and sufficient. When I converted my new home nine years later I had to have two twin sockets on every wall and even more in the lounge, because like many householders I had acquired a computer, printer and fax, an answering machine, a cordless phone, a mobile phone and a video.

In my kitchen I had a microwave, a juicer, a blender and my daughter's steam-sterilizing unit all competing for sockets. Sometimes I think of the home my grandmother had only fifteen years ago and how baffled she would have been by all our gadgets.

Worst of all, I noticed I was sleeping under two bedside electric lights, with my answering machine, my cordless phone and the stereo and alarm clock all plugged in and sitting on my bedside table.

If you want to look and feel younger you must limit the amount of electricity that is around you as you sleep. It helps to be aware of the electricity around you during the day, but night-time exposure to electricity is even more important because we stay in one place for several hours, so all the electricity by our beds, especially that near to our pillows, is passing in and out of our bodies and our cells all night long, disrupting cell activity at the time when cells are programmed to do the very important work of cell regeneration and repair which is essential to our looks and health.

While I was studying the effects of electricity on the body I made some very easy changes. I put my stereo on the floor further away from me, but near enough for me to listen to my becoming younger tape at night. I got rid of my alarm clock – however, if you feel one is essential, get a very small battery-operated model, *not* a fluorescent one.

I also moved my answering machine, and although I do occasionally love to watch television in bed, I have moved my TV right to the end of my room and am planning to put it in a cabinet of sorts to screen the electromagnetic rays that come from it.

We have moved so quickly into a world where we are bombarded by electricity, and are seemingly always in the company of something electric, yet we don't fully know the effects of, say, using a mobile phone for hours at a time. They don't come with any warning, but they do have a detrimental effect on our body cells, as does spending too long in too close proximity to any electrical appliance.

We are being bombarded day and night by electromagnetic rays, and the effects of electrical pollution are being linked to many illnesses and ailments including low sperm count, infertility, ME, migraines, cancer, depression and ADD, to name just a few. Scientists and doctors are now becoming increasingly aware of the negative and debilitating effects that too much or too frequent exposure even to household electricity can have on the body.

In most modern homes, without us being aware of it, electromagnetic rays are passing through our delicate body cells day and night, often twenty-four hours a day. Our bodies are not designed to cope with this, and it has happened far too fast for the human body to adapt to electrical pollution. You can feel the electricity if you run your hand over the television screen; just switching on a lamp will cause the brain's rhythms to instantly change; and if you hold a strip light near an electricity pylon it can come on just because of the electricity that is there.

People whose homes are near to electricity sub-stations or power lines and pylons do seem to have a higher incidence of illnesses, including some forms of cancer, Alzheimer's and Parkinson's disease, as well as depression, insomnia and lethargy. The same thing can occur in homes that have an abundance of electrical equipment in almost every room. I find this especially a matter for concern with children – there is a significant amount of childhood cancer and leukaemia that is being linked to children living and sleeping too near generators or other major sources of electricity.

Many people just don't want to believe this – however, it has finally been accepted and proved that over-exposure to X-ray machines can cause cancer and other illnesses. Ross Adey, chairman of the US National Council on Radiation Protection, states that there is proof that even very low levels of exposure to EMFs (Electromagnetic Fields) are linked to long-term effects on health. The report suggests limiting our exposure to a maximum of 0.2 microtesias, the measurement of leakage.

In most homes the levels measure about 0.1 to 0.2 – however, the closer you are to an appliance, the higher the level. Being too close to the television or radio, and even being too close to a hairdryer, can immediately push the level up to 7.

Many ordinary household appliances can emit 100 times the limit recognized as safe as soon as we are within 12 inches of them, so the further away we are, the safer the limit becomes. Even with something as simple as vacuuming you can benefit your health by keeping the vacuum cleaner at arm's length rather than having it right next to your body.

In Britain the measure for electromagnetic fields is measured in nanotesias. The safe level, according to leading Swedish and American reports, is 200 nanotesias, but there is no safe level recognized in Britain yet. To keep to this safe level you need to sleep at least 4 feet away from electricity meters, clock radios and night storage heaters, or the level can go up enormously.

I realize this sounds alarming, but the good news is that these same levels go down significantly as you move further away from the electricity. Moving a foot away makes a huge difference, and is so easy to do.

I am not suggesting that we give up our electrical devices, but that we become aware of the negative side effects of them. Don't let children sleep with a computer or television by the bed − move these as far away from the bedhead as possible, preferably outside the bedroom. Put stereos, radios and alarm clocks on the floor, especially with very small children.

The effects of electromagnetic rays passing through the body constantly during the night are very detrimental to looking and feeling young. To look young, and to have good skin and good health, we need to have strong, resilient cells − we must protect our cells from electrical pollution, especially at night, since this is when cells regenerate and repair themselves.

Here Are Some Very Easy Changes You Can Make to Benefit Your Health and to Remain Younger

DON'T fall asleep watching television in bed.

Watch television from a distance of about 3 feet, preferably 4 feet.

Move as many surplus electrical appliances out of your bedroom as you can.

Place those that you feel you must keep as far away from your bed as possible.

If you feel you must have a bedside clock, have a tiny one.

Downsize your bedside light – push it further away from your pillows. Aim to sleep at least 4 feet away from electricity even if it means you have to push lamps away at night.

Sleep at least 4 feet away from storage heaters, electricity meters and clock radios.

Don't sit or stand too close to electrical appliances.

Don't sleep with your head near a radiator.

Don't use an electric blanket, especially an overblanket designed to be left on all night.

Remember your hairdresser's advice – keep the dryer more than 14 inches away from your head. This advice was given to protect the hair from burning, but it will protect your body too.

Take high doses of vitamin C, at least 1,000 mg daily, as it offers protection against radiation. So do sulphur and spirulina. Take at least ten capsules of spirulina daily, and treble that amount if you work around electricity. Foods rich in sulphur are broccoli, Brussels sprouts, cabbage, cauliflower and eggs.

Cut down your use of appliances, and when you do use them, use them for less time.

Switch your cordless phone back to a normal handset phone.

Be aware of how long you are on a mobile phone. Don't use it when you can use a regular phone, and the same with cordless phones – use a normal handset phone whenever possible, as both mobile phones and cordless phones are very highly charged.

When you are using a mobile phone, keep changing sides as you hold it. Don't clamp the phone to your ear or mouth – hold it a little way away and don't stay on the phone for too long.

Use a protective screen if you use a computer and take frequent breaks – maybe go outside, away from electricity, for a few minutes every few hours. Apparently spider plants and cactus are very good at absorbing radiation from computer terminals, so place a spider plant behind and a cactus in front of your computer.

Notice how much you are around electricity and make changes that are appropriate and effective for you, your health and your looks.

Make some decisions to restrict small children's exposure to electricity.

My 7-year-old loves being on the computer, but I would not want her to have a computer in her room. If your children are older you may be able to place a computer in the kitchen – it is less anti-social and isolating there too.

My daughter also loves listening to Enid Blyton stories on tape, and adores going to bed listening to the Famous Five. She used to use one of our portable cassette players, but now I have bought her a children's battery-operated tape recorder because it has much lower levels of electromagnetic rays.

I also encourage her to sit further away from the television. However, she is a twentieth-century child – I can't remove her from electricity nor would I want to. The same applies to me – I love some of my gadgets and would not want to give them up. I wouldn't change my computer for a manual typewriter, but I have made very many changes that have not inconvenienced me at all and I urge you to do the same.

Exercise and Ageing

A feeble body enfeebles the mind.
JEAN-JACQUES ROUSSEAU

If you want to become and remain younger, it is vital to engage in some form of regular exercise because exercising has a very important role to play in slowing down ageing. In numerous tests exercising has been proved to prevent muscle wastage and bone loss, while maintaining agility and boosting energy levels. Regular and gentle exercise alone will reverse ageing by five years in men and four in women, according to scientist Dr Richard Hochschild, while regular aerobic exercise can cause the heart to be biologically ten years younger.

Studies by Harvard and Stanford Universities involving 17,000 men and women, carried out over fifty years, found that exercise unquestionably delays ageing.

Tufts University ran an eight-week strength-training pro-gramme by taking the oldest and frailest people in an old people's home and involving them in a gentle programme of weight-bearing exercises. The results found that women and men between the ages of 87 and 96 years old could increase their muscle size and strength by 300 per cent within just eight weeks, while also improving co-ordination and balance.

Tests carried out at the Andrus Gerontology Center in Cali-fornia took over 200 inactive 60–70-year-olds, started them on a programme of moderate exercise, and found they became as fit as people thirty years younger with energy levels to match.

In another study, people between the ages of 80 and 90 who did gentle and regular exercise doubled their strength. Even gentle exercise will reverse ageing by 10 per cent. Swimming, walking, yoga and t'ai chi are all excellent, because they are easy to do and don't put any strain on the body.

Exercise can reverse the major effects of ageing such as blood pressure, increased body fat, decreasing muscle mass, hearing and bone density. Exercise strengthens heart muscles so the heart is a more efficient pump.

Exercise can even improve hearing and memory. Exercise also helps constipation greatly, because it improves bowel transit time by up to 56 per cent. Exercise has a positive effect on motilin, a gastro–intestinal hormone linked to faster transit time of waste through the bowel. Exercise also improves blood flow to the intestines, improving bowel movements in a safe and comfortable way. Constipation is itself very ageing, because it sends toxins that should be eliminated back into the blood-stream, causing us to feel sluggish, sometimes causing head-aches, causing the skin to look tired and unhealthy and to break out in spots. Constipation can also cause varicose veins.

You don't need to overdo exercise or strain your body to get excellent results – gentle exercise is just as effective. Bengt Saltin, a Swedish physiologist, ran some tests in the 1960s in which he had five men, two of whom were athletes, lie in bed for three weeks as he monitored their bodies' physiological response to extended disuse. His results showed that within just twenty-one days their aerobic capacity diminished so rapidly that it was equivalent to twenty years of ageing. When they began to exercise again they were able to reverse the results, further proof that exercise reverses ageing.

If you stay inactive for twenty-four hours your muscle tissue starts to decline. If you have to endure even short periods of bed rest your bones quickly lose minerals and become weaker and more prone to breaking, your muscles shrink, and you begin to experience skin and muscle wasting. The major cause of muscle loss as we age is being inactive. Activity is an enemy of ageing – if you plan to become and remain younger you must take part in some form of regular exercise. We can improve our bodies by using them more, not less.

In tribes and cultures where daily exercise is the norm, osteoporosis and osteoarthritis are virtually unknown. It has been proved again and again that we cannot wear out our bodies by using them the way they were meant to be used, which is by being active, and although it is true that excessive exercise can have a detrimental effect on joints, what we are talking about here is gentle, easy, regular exercise that can be enjoyed at any age.

Deepak Chopra has said: *We don't wear out, and too much rest can be the worst thing for our body and for muscle and skeletal wasting.* Not exercising is harder work than exercising – Dr De Vries at the Gerontology Center in California said: *It is the body so unused to activity that tires at the slightest effort.*

The great thing about exercise is that once you begin to do it you start to enjoy it and want to continue. It is never ever too late to begin an exercise programme, as the Tufts University programme shows – even to begin exercising at 90 will benefit your body, but don't wait, start to exercise now and you will benefit in so many ways.

When I was at school I hated all forms of exercise. I was definitely unsporty and was classed as 'no good at sport'. When I left school believing that I hated exercise and was hopeless at it, I didn't exercise at all for several years. I regret now that I was not athletic and missed out on all the pleasures of sport.

Some years later, because I was studying physiology and because my boyfriend was a professional footballer, I almost by accident got involved in the exercise boom and after training became an exercise instructor. I found that I loved exercising and was very good at it and very good at teaching it. I found I was naturally supple – I could do the splits with ease and had lots of stamina. People in my class found it hard to believe I had not always been that way and had in fact only been exercising for a relatively short period of time.

I taught classes in London, Los Angeles, Chicago, Washington DC and New York, and appeared on *Newsnight* and other television programmes discussing the merits of exercise. I got a lot of very positive articles in the press for my teaching – one said I was the most professional and thorough exercise teacher in London. I often wondered how my teachers at school would feel about that, since I was always told I was hopeless at sport at school.

No matter what you have believed about yourself and exercising, it is never too late to begin. Like me you might just surprise yourself and find that you love it, especially if you make a point of finding some kind of exercise that you enjoy in an environment that you like. It is important to find a form of exercise you really like so you will stick with it – if you participate in any form of exercise and dislike it you won't get beneficial results. It also helps to cross-train, to vary your exercise, so you could swim or walk, do yoga and some weight-bearing exercise every week. Sex is very good exercise too.

It is just as effective to exercise little and often, and if you can find something like badminton or tennis that is social and enjoyable, even better, as you have more chance of sticking to it.

Whatever form of exercise you choose to do, you must include weight-bearing exercise in your programme because it prevents the thinning of the bones that results in osteoporosis. Bones are full of blood vessels and are constantly making new cells, and exercise that puts weight on the bones is essential to prevent bone loss. Lack of exercise is indicated as one of the causes of bone loss, and it is important to begin an easy weight-bearing routine before you actually need to, and to make it a way of life. Don't wait until it is too late, because lack of exercise ultimately leads to bone loss.

It was found that astronauts who had spent weeks in space in a weightless state that put no weight on their bones suffered dramatic bone loss that was only remedied with weight-bearing exercises. Astronauts have also become extremely prone to depression when their bodies have been forced to be inactive because of weightlessness.

By taking up regular weight-bearing exercise you will increase stress on bone, which helps to increase bone density that in turn strengthens the bone. Women gradually lose bone mass from 35 onwards; this increases more rapidly after menopause, and bones become more brittle with the decrease of oestrogen, but putting weight on the bones through weight-bearing exercises can counteract much of this loss of bone mass.

Weight training is also known as strength training. You don't have to become a weight-lifter to benefit from weight-bearing exercises, because using your own body as the weight is also an excellent form of weight training. You can find a programme in your local gym involving the use of small hand weights or using the weight-training machines; many exercise classes use small hand weights as part of the class. Weightlifter's bones are nearly 50 per cent thicker and stronger than those of non-weightlifters.

If the idea of going to a gym does not appeal to you, you can do weight-bearing exercises at home utilizing your body weight as resistance. Doing press-ups or standing press-ups against a wall is a way of using your own body weight, as are stomach exercises and leg and arm exercises using your own body weight as resistance.

Even walking is a weight-bearing exercise because you are using a combination of gravity and your body weight on your legs and bones, which become stronger as more weight is brought to bear upon them. Walking also exercises your heart and lungs while toning muscles and burning calories. Walking for thirty minutes five or six times a week is as effective in slowing down and reversing ageing as running forty miles a week. You don't have to work out hard, to push yourself or to drip sweat to get the benefits that will allow you to defy ageing.

Doing weight-bearing exercises three times a week will lower your risk of osteoporosis, as will two hours of walking every week. If your excuse has been *I don't have time to exercise*, you need to know that ten minutes of running or jogging a day will give you the same benefits (but you need to run six days out of seven).

Weight training or strength training will also improve your posture, your shape and your strength while it improves the density of bones that decreases with age. When muscle mass and strength diminish we become weaker, and muscle is then replaced by fat, but if you participate in strength training you can maintain muscle tissue as you age. This will keep you leaner with a better metabolism too, because muscle tissue is more metabolically active than fat tissue.

The University of Pittsburgh School of Medicine studied 500 women for three years, recording their weight, triglycerides, cholesterol and blood pressure at the beginning and at the end of the three-year period. They found that the women who exercised gained the least weight and had the healthiest blood cholesterol levels. The results of their tests, and those undertaken by other institutes set up to study the connection between exercise and ageing, show that exercise strengthens bones, prevents osteoporosis and weight increase, while improving triglycerides, cholesterol and diastolic blood pressure.

Further studies also show that exercise can decrease cholesterol levels while increasing metabolic rate, bone strength and memory, especially short-term memory. As we get older our brain cells may receive fewer nutrients and less oxygen, and regular exercise can maintain high nutrient and oxygen levels which in turn fight ageing.

Exercise boosts endorphin levels and can decrease PMS.

From birth we make a hormone called Human Growth Hormone, known as HGH. This hormone does very important work in the body – primarily it increases muscle tone and lean mass while stimulating tissue growth and the growth of bones and organs. Human Growth Hormone is also responsible for enhancing our flexibility, thickening our muscles and maintaining healthy body tissues.

HGH is released naturally into our bloodstream during the night, but it begins to decline at around the age of 30 and continues to drop until by the age of 60 a third of men have either very little or no HGH, while women still have some but not enough.

However, after each session of intense exercise or a workout we receive a dose of HGH. Therefore you have it within your power to continue to receive a steady supply of HGH by exercising regularly. It must be a form of exercise that makes you work (but it does not have to be excessively hard work), and weight training again comes into this category perfectly.

Tests done in America in 1989 gave twenty-eight men aged from 60 to 80 weekly injections of Human Growth Hormone and they very quickly reversed the age of their bodies by twenty years. More studies from Florida show that 60-year-olds who had not exercised for years, and had no muscle tone for fifteen years, once put on to a weight-training programme could gain muscle mass equal to that of someone of 21. As a bonus, their energy levels could match someone in their early twenties as well.

This is all the proof you need that exercise can and does fight ageing, so you can be as strong and as fit in your seventies and eighties as you were in your twenties, with a consistent supply of HGH contributing to good muscle tone and flexibility and continuing to build bones, organs and healthy body tissue no matter what your age.

One of the reasons alcohol is so ageing is because while you are drinking alcohol you will temporarily suppress the production of growth hormones which keep your cells vigorous and active. Drinking too frequently may have a very detrimental effect on the production of growth hormones, as blood levels of growth hormones fall after every drinking bout.

Heavy drinking also causes a dramatic increase of free radicals in our bodies and is very damaging to the skin – it can lead to blotchiness, broken veins, enlarged pores, puffiness, decreased skin tone, thin, stressed, tired skin, and rhinophyma, a condition that causes the nose to become larger and redder. Alcohol can also disrupt periods and contribute to early menopause. It can increase oestrogen levels by 20–30 per cent during mid-cycle. Alcohol dramatically ages the skin and lowers our bone mass, which can lead to osteoporosis. As we age our bodies are less and less able to deal with alcohol. Alcohol also dehydrates our cells, impairs the flow of proteins to the cells and deprives the cells of oxygen, leading to rapid wrinkles and accelerated ageing.

If you are living a life of constant stress, or if you feel stressed all the time, you are undoubtedly affecting your ageing process and accelerating it. This is because 90 per cent of our cells' energy is needed for cell renewal, and in times of stress the whole process of rebuilding is set aside. This is OK if it only happens occasionally, but in the long term it has an appalling effect on our bodies and can age us far too quickly. There are so many methods available to us to counteract stress: for instance, you can use massage, relaxation techniques and meditation. You can learn deep breathing, which helps greatly. Taking regular exercise, such as swimming, yoga or walking, is a great stress-reducer and yet another reason for regular exercise.

If you find a form of exercise that you love, that you find exciting or thrilling or even adventurous, you will begin to age wonderfully, because excitement, thrills and adventure release very different chemicals in our brain and increase the flow of blood and oxygen to our body tissues. You don't need to go rock-climbing to feel excitement – many people find that going to step aerobics or low-impact aerobic or yoga classes makes them feel so good that they find exercising compelling and fit it into their schedule as a must or a priority, even finding classes to take while on holiday. When I was teaching, occasionally someone in my class would say *This feels even better than sex*. A girl in my class once said to me *This is better than taking drugs – I much prefer the high I get from exercising and it only costs me £3.00 a class to achieve it.*

Feet shorten as we age – the arch of the foot collapses and many older people shuffle instead of walking. There is a specific exercise that will lengthen the foot arch and is very easy to do. To keep the arch of the foot in good condition, kneel on a mat or carpet without shoes and with your bottom resting on your heels and your palms or fingers placed on the floor either side of your knees. Keeping your body weight distributed between your bottom and hands, and your back reasonably straight, lift both your knees together off the floor and hold that position. The higher you can raise your knees, the more of a stretch you will feel in the arch of your foot. Do this several times and hold it for about twenty seconds. You can get just as good results if you kneel, but have your arms out ahead of you and hold on to a chair or table for extra support.

Walter Boritz, a specialist in ageing at Stanford University, studied what happens to the body when we stop exercising and found that when the body is removed from physical exercise this alone will accelerate the ageing process. Our bodies need to exercise and like to be used, and when we stop exercising our bodies the heart becomes weaker, the arteries become older, the cardiovascular system becomes poorer, muscle, skeletal and bone wasting begins a rapid onset, the bones become fragile, osteoporosis becomes a bigger risk, depression and weight gain become more apparent, and the body ages biologically so that it is older than its chronological years. When we stop using our bodies they begin to fade and wither away. Dr Boritz called this Disuse Syndrome, when the body stops exercising, leading to rapid, premature ageing.

Dr Boritz has shown time and time again that lack of exercise produces changes in the body that parallel the changes we experience with ageing. He believes some instances of rapid ageing are not symptoms of ageing at all, but symptoms of disuse of the body.

Tests done on inactive people showed that exercise would reverse their symptoms and prevent them recurring for many years. Dr Boritz said *So exceptional is the ability of regular exercise to reverse ageing, it seems extremely unlikely that any further drug or physician-oriented technique will approach such a benefit.*

Quote
To win back my youth there is nothing I wouldn't do except take exercise, get up early or be a useful member of the community.

OSCAR WILDE

Skin Brushing and Ageing

Skin brushing has the most amazing benefits that really can't be justified in print. After just a few days of skin brushing you will find that you have masses more energy and your whole system feels clean and invigorated, while your skin will already look and feel better and younger.

It has been practised in Europe for centuries, especially at spas, where it is used to stimulate lymphatic drainage and improve waste elimination via the skin's surface. It is often a very important part of natural healing and remedies. Lymphatic drainage, correctly and professionally used, has been an effective treatment for cancer and other serious illnesses as well as for fatigue and lethargy. It is also used as a beauty and anti-ageing treatment.

Skin brushing stimulates circulation and helps pump blood down through the veins and up through the arteries, feeding essential organs. It stimulates and cleanses the lymphatic system, promoting super-efficient lymphatic drainage while boosting the nervous system and improving the metabolic system.

When you skin brush over the major lymph glands – which are situated in the armpits, by the groin, behind elbows and knees and either side of the throat – where waste fluid is deposited, it will stimulate the elimination of cellulite. Cellulite is caused by impacted lymph and other waste material, along with fat, water and toxins, becoming trapped in areas of the body – usually the bottom and legs – and held by toughened connective tissue.

If you are serious about wanting to be free of cellulite, then skin brush twice daily to stimulate the tissues beneath the skin (but not just before sleeping, as its invigorating effect may keep you awake). Follow with a warm then a cold shower to improve circulation and elimination, moving the shower head from the feet upwards. End the shower by running cold or tepid water over the base of the skull and down your spine for thirty seconds – this will allow your glandular system, nervous system and other organs to work much more efficiently and can even stop you getting colds.

Skin brushing is excellent for exfoliation, since it removes dead surface skin layers along with other toxins, metabolic wastes and bacteria shed by cells. It keeps our pores unclogged and improves the skin's elimination ability.

We have more lymph in our body than we have blood – however, the lymph does not have a pump and relies on us taking deep, diaphragmatic breaths and moving a lot to allow it to move around the body. Muscle movement and gravity are meant to keep lymph flowing, pump lymph back through its channels and eliminate waste. Running and other forms of aerobic exercise encourage correct lymph activity and flush wastes from tissue fluids. Using a mini trampoline for just a few minutes daily is excellent for promoting correct lymph movement.

We eliminate through our skin, lungs, kidneys and colon. Up to a third of waste elimination is through the skin – our sweat glands are meant to expel a minimum of one pound of waste material daily. When they don't, because our bodies are not working at peak efficiency, this toxic waste can remain in our system causing all kinds of damage.

When Red Indians became very old and wanted to die because they felt they were a liability to a tribe on the move, they would tie their wrists together, sit under a tree, hook their tied arms over a branch, and would die before morning because this action had such a negative effect on lymph movement.

Our skin is the largest organ in the body that has two-way elimination – it uses perspiration to flush elements out of our bodies and is able to absorb other elements by means of sunshine, aromatherapy oils, herbal rubs and balms, and so on. After the brain, the skin is the most complex organ, made up of, among other things, nerve endings, blood vessels, sweat glands, muscles, sensory cells and receptors that respond to heat, to cold, to touch and wonderfully to skin brushing. Skin brushing regularly for only a few minutes daily can be as effective as thirty minutes of exercise, because it improves physical tone and muscle tone. It has a very important place in making us feel and look years younger while improving our sense of well-being. It is very easy to do, and soon becomes an automatic part of your morning routine, the benefits easily outweighing the small investment of time required to skin brush properly.

You must use a natural vegetable bristle brush, found in most health food shops and chemists.

Skin brushing is best done in the morning, prior to showering. Your body and the brush must be dry.

Begin with the soles of the feet. Brush in between the toes, then brush vigorously up your legs, front and back, using firm sweeping strokes.

From the thighs, brush towards the groin, but not over it, which is the major lymph gland and store.

Over the stomach, brush in a circular, clockwise movement following the natural line of the colon, and repeat about ten times.

Brush the palms of your hands then the backs, then move up the arms and shoulders.

Brush upwards towards the heart, then downwards once you are above the heart.

Brush downwards over the neck, throat and chest, then brush your upper and lower back and bottom.

Always avoid the nipples, groin itself, very irritated or infected skin, severe varicose veins and the face, although you can get special softer brushes for facial brushing from the Body Shop and Boots.

You can brush the scalp to stimulate hair growth and to improve the hair's texture and condition. Skin brush more gently initially and more firmly over time. In the beginning do it daily for three months, then several times each week.

Spend about five minutes on skin brushing and follow with a hot shower, ending with a few moments of cold water, or lukewarm if you can't bear the cold spray.

Look after your body brush by washing it once a week using

natural soap. Rinse it thoroughly, dry it naturally, and don't share it with anyone.

Sleep and Ageing

Proper sleep is essential if you want to age well.

Not only is the right amount of sleep vital (and this varies – some people need more than others), but when and how you sleep is also important.

Cells repair and regenerate themselves at night. It has been said that humans sleep so that the process of cell regeneration can be carried out – animals that have a shorter lifespan and don't have any cell turnover don't sleep at all, such as butterflies, earthworms and mayflies. Dolphins and sharks don't sleep, they only rest. Elephants only sleep for two hours in a twenty-four-hour period.

Cell regeneration seems to occur at around 2 a.m., so it is important to be asleep by then, at least most of the time. Staying up late on a regular basis is very ageing – it has been said that one hour of sleep before midnight is equivalent to two hours of sleep after.

We are all cyclical by nature, and our body has its own body clock. The menstrual cycle is a good example of this. Our body clock is designed to do certain things at certain times – for example, exercise is better in the morning, digestion is better in the afternoon, and sleep is better at night.

It is fine to have some late nights, to stay up late having fun, but make sure you compensate for that by having some early nights and sleeping well at other times.

It is hard for the body to catch up on lost sleep, and the body functions much better with consistent patterns of sleep rather than with sleep patterns that are erratic and constantly changing. Regular sleep is needed so that the brain can stay alert and function efficiently.

Females who have to work through the night, for example

casino staff, nurses, airline staff, those in the police force and the emergency services, can be more prone to hormonal problems, erratic periods and conception problems, and this has been linked to the fact that the body's natural rhythms become disturbed. Night workers have a higher record of colds and depression, and a much weaker immune system, because the body never truly adapts to the reversing of the sleeping and waking cycle. We are meant to sleep when it's dark and rise when it's light. If you want to have great skin and consistent energy and to look and feel younger, you must get enough sleep and at the right time of night too – this becomes even more important as we get older.

Even the way you sleep can have an effect on your skin. A wrinkle is a crease in the skin that occurs when the collagen beneath it is imprinted by a continual muscle action, such as frowning, smiling, squinting, grimacing, etc. People with facial paralysis often have unlined skin because they don't have these muscle actions. Many people sleep in a way that causes their face, their skin, to 'pleat' while they sleep. By nature we appear to sleep more on our right side than our left during the night, and some people notice they have slightly more, or more deeply pronounced, lines and wrinkles on the right side. If you sleep on your stomach or with your face pressed into a pillow, this will leave a wrinkle memory in your skin – in other words, a premature wrinkle that could have been avoided.

Sleeping with a lot of pillows makes this much worse. Sleep with only one pillow, and choose a pillow that is quite flat. If you have been used to two or three plump, squashy pillows you will miss them at first, but soon not even notice the difference. It is best to sleep on your back or side and with your pillow under your neck rather than your head if you wish to avoid lines and wrinkles.

If you don't find it easy to get to sleep quickly you can burn some lavender oil, which is very relaxing. Or you can listen to a self-hypnosis tape to induce sleep – you can use a tape specially made for insomnia, or make your own tape of the cell regeneration script, which is intended to be played prior to sleeping at night and will make you very relaxed. You can also use self-hypnosis or relaxation methods to enjoy perfect sleep every night.

Sleep in a room that is well ventilated.

Don't sleep with the heating on unless it is exceptionally cold.

Don't sleep with your head by a radiator or close to electrical appliances, because of the effects of electromagnetic rays passing into your body during the night.

Don't overstimulate your mind just before bed with scary films or novels if you don't sleep well.

Don't eat a lot of food before going to bed (see the section on digestion and ageing).

Quote
Sleep that knits up the ravelled sleeve of care.

SHAKESPEARE

Your final exercises on this, your final day of taking action to look and feel younger, are to:

1. Include the wonderfoods in your diet. Copy out the list of wonderfoods and pin it to your fridge door or keep it in your wallet or Filofax. Make sure you include these foods in your shopping and whenever you eat out.

   Go through your fridge and cupboards and get rid of processed and junk food. Eliminate saturated fats from your home. Stop using animal fats to cook with, and use more herbs and spices from the list of superfoods, such as ginger, thyme and garlic. Buy more organic foods – most big supermarkets are selling more organic produce.

2. List the vitamins that you need to take, and ensure that you order or purchase an adequate supply.

3. Decide how you can exercise and make it a lifelong part of your lifestyle. Find a class to go to regularly or exercise with a friend; make exercising a compulsive habit. Even walking further instead of driving, and taking the stairs rather than the lift, will make a difference over time.

4. Move your electrical appliances, especially those near your bed. Put some appliances outside the room, or at least on the floor or away from pillows as you sleep. Put plants in front of your computer. Move seating further away from televisions, stereos and radiators. Re-install your normal handset telephones and use them more and your cordless or mobile phones less.

5. Buy digestive enzymes and a body brush and use them regularly.

6. Take away surplus pillows or put them on the floor before you sleep.

You will find making these lifestyle changes easy, and you will find yourself making more and more of them because the results will be so visible and because you will feel so much better and therefore motivated to continue.

Quote

If youth knew how, if old age were able.

HENRI ESTIENNE

COMMON DENOMINATORS OF 100-YEAR-OLDS

Many tests have been done on centenarians to find out the secrets of those who live to be 100 or more. These tests are quite diverse and often produce conflicting information. It is becoming easier to study people of 100 because every year there are more of them to study. In 1951 in Britain there were 300 100-year-olds while today there are over 4,500. The number of people of 100 years of age doubles every ten years. In France, where they have the next longest-living women to Japan, there were 200 100-year-olds in 1953, while today there are over 6,000. These figures are heady stuff, because they show us that the number of people reaching their 100th birthday has increased over thirty times. Within the next fifty years the number will reach over 150,000. We are all going to live longer, and being 100 years old will become absolutely routine. Genes will only be partly to do with this, since even if both your parents live long lives that may only add about three years to your life. Having parents who live long lives, however, will help you have an expectation that you will do the same.

In numerous tests carried out on centenarians in Japan, America and Europe, the common denominators that they shared were a feeling of being loved, of feeling respected, valued and appreciated. They all had some degree of independence, had usually worked hard throughout their lives, and took an active interest in life in general and in their own lives in particular. On the whole they wanted to go on living and had a reason to do so.

The results of studies on diet were vastly different, but they had obviously eaten less processed and chemically treated food when they were younger. This is a relatively recent addition to food, and the centenarians' diet consisted of much more natural food – predominantly grains, vegetables and fruits, and less meat, fat and sugar. Another common denominator was that almost all had not over-eaten. Some of them had smoked, but they had been exposed to less pollution in general.

Many societies and groups of longer-living old people eat a diet that includes a particular food, such as yoghurt, apricots, grains and honey. In his book *Seven Health Secrets from the Hive*, Charles Robson documents tribes in which people are chronologically very old yet actually stay very young and healthy on diets rich in bee pollen, propolis and royal jelly.

Activity was a trait all the centenarians shared. They had all been active, they had all worked hard, often at some form of manual labour, and in their time of course housework was hard manual work. Many of them still did some housework or cooking, and they had usually had a healthy sex life, which many of them continued into their eighties.

They were mentally active too, and stimulated their brains by being involved in things and maintaining an interest in current affairs. They had hobbies, and were interested in what was going on around them. They had a good sense of humour, laughed a lot, still had fun, and did not feel they were a burden to others. They shared in common a vitality and energy and radiance about life; they were generally optimistic and positive in their attitude and were happy and fulfilled.

What these tests of 'young old people' from around the world show is that personality, especially a strong and positive personality, is as strong a factor in staying young as making changes in your health. Reports from the Medical Research

Council show that wilful, cantankerous old people can live longer. Similar studies with chronic illness show that the same wilful cantankerous character has a high disposition to survive illness at any age. A desire not to conform or be passive is talked about in Dr Berie Siega's book *Love, Medicine and Miracles*, in which he says if you want to survive a chronic illness have the word 'uncooperative' written on your medical notes.

EPILOGUE

Well done. You have finished this book and learned so much. You will have a new way of thinking now and a different belief system to when you began this book. You have begun to achieve your goals and you can remain younger. Over the last ten days you have learned how to change your thoughts, your beliefs, your language and even your physiology in the area of ageing. You have also learned how your mind works, how to make affirmations work for you and how to become a physical expression of your affirmations. You have been shown how to programme your mind to age excellently, how to use self-hypnosis to get even more positive results, how to visualize being younger, how to set and achieve goals for ageing well and how to reclaim and redefine a wonderful, positive and ageless image of yourself. You have done some physical tests to prove to yourself that you have a wonderful power over your body and that no outside source can influence and affect your body to the extent that you can. You have done a lot of testing of your biological age and you will be able to refer to the test for ageing successfully again and again and notice how much better your score is, especially as you have also learned to use the wonderful anti-ageing properties of vitamins, exercise and certain foods. Finally, you learned that moving electrical appliances, skin brushing and enjoying proper sleep and digestion can allow you to live years longer while looking years younger. You have learned to become more like Sara and less like Jill and this can become for you a lifelong habit. You can move on from one great achievement to another in the area of staying young.

You may find yourself wanting to read this book or favourite parts of it again and I recommend that you do. It is a very good idea to return to this book maybe every six months or every time you celebrate another birthday and do some refresher exercises to remind yourself that you will choose how young you want to feel and be.

Congratulations for staying with the book. I applaud you for doing all the work. The rewards you will get from the investment you made by fully participating in this programme are endless. It is up to you to implement these changes and to continue with this new way of thinking, this new belief system and attitude and these new habits and lifestyle changes. It is up to you to go on making them work for you in all aspects of your life and of course to believe and know you can do it. As long as you do this you cannot and will not return to your old ways of thinking and feeling.

It is also vital to be calm and positive and to always have an optimistic view of ageing, since to age well we need to be free from panic, we need to be calm, to have unshakeable confidence and conviction in our bodies' ability to regenerate themselves, to bring about their own healing and repair. To know and believe that we can stay younger at any age.

You will get ill and tired much less if you feel good about yourself and take full responsibility for how you feel, not just now but all the time. You will age remarkably better if you feel happy, so it really is important to laugh every day, to have a sense of humour, to be childlike, not always to take things and life too seriously. People have cured themselves of illness by something called laughter therapy, which involves laughing daily. Norman Cousins, in his book *Anatomy of an Illness*, describes the techniques he used to cure himself of cancer.

These included installing a video and television in his room and renting as many funny films and series as he could and laughing for hours every day, which caused his body to make the healing chemicals he needed to fight the disease.

Good luck in living a longer, healthier, younger life. I know you are going to live longer – make sure you enjoy the process and please let me know how you have changed and what has happened to you since you became a participant in the philosophy of *Forever Young*. I *love* hearing from people who have benefited from this process, so please write to me – maybe you will become a part of my next book. I have so enjoyed writing this book and showing you the things that have made a huge difference in my life and that of my clients; maybe I will meet you at one of my seminars. Goodbye.

Things do get better as we age, especially if we can see things in a better light. As Mark Twain said: *My father was an idiot when I was fourteen. When I was twenty-one I was astonished at how much he had learnt in seven years.*

SOURCES

Ginger: research from Odense University, Denmark. Dr Tariq Mustafa associate professor at the Institute of Biology, Odense found ginger to inhibit two of the enzymes responsible for inflammation in arthritis.

Selenium: research by Dr Donald Lisk, Professor of Toxicology at Cornell University.

Cabbage: Dr H. Leon Bradlow, Strang Cornell Cancer Research Laboratory, New York City, found 70 per cent of women who ate cabbage began burning off dangerous oestrogen within five days.

Citrus fruits: the National Cancer Institute class oranges as a total package of every anti-cancer inhibitor in existence.

Grapes: the University of California and the University of Wisconsin discovered three glasses of purple grape juice have anti-clogging effects in arteries.

Tomatoes: studies in Germany and Italy.

Garlic: studies in the *Journal of the Royal College of Physicians*.

Soya: studies by Dr Ann R. Kennedy, University of Pennsylvania School of Medicine, find Bowman-Birk inhibitor, a protease inhibitor found in soya, so versatile against cancers that Dr Kennedy calls it *a universal cancer preventative agent*. Dr Stephen Barnes, University of Alabama, Birmingham, says soya beans

inhibit breast tumour growth in models of breast cancer. Dr
Mark Messina, *Journal of the National Cancer Institute*, co-author
of *The Simple Soybean and Your Health*, states that your risk of
cancer doubles without soya beans.

Brazil nuts and selenium levels: *Journal of Food Safety*, 1989. Dr
Hertog at the Dutch National Institute of Public Health,
researching quercetin intake for heart protection, found that of
800 elderly Dutch men those consuming a steady supply of
quercetin reduced their risk of heart attack by 60 per cent.

Ginkgo Biloba: *British Journal of Clinical Pharmacology*.

Rules of the Mind used with permission of Gil Boyne, Westwood
Publishing Company and adapted to ageing by Marisa Peer.

Recommended Reading for Anti-Ageing

Biomarkers by William Evans and Brian Rosenberg of Tufts
University talks about the ten markers for age that are now
believed to be reversible.

Mindfulness by Dr Ellen Langer, Addison Wesley Press.

Ageless Body, Timeless Mind by Deepak Chopra, Random House.

The New Supernutrition by Dr Richard Passwater, Pocket Books.

Love, Medicine and Miracles by Bernie Siegel, Harper & Row.

Fats that Heal Fats that Kill by Dr Udo Erasmus, Alive Books.

Please write to:
Marisa Peer
c/o The Christopher Little Literary Agency,
48 Walham Grove,
London
SW6 1QR.